Person to Person

A guide to the care of those with failing mental powers

by Tom Kitwood and Kathleen Bredin

Second Edition

Foreword by John P. Wattis MB DPM FRC PSYCH
Consultant Geriatrician St. James's University Hospital Leeds

GALE CENTRE PUBLICATION WHITAKERS WAY LOUGHTON ESSEX IG10 1SQ

i

First published in 1991 by Bradford Dementia Research Group

Second Edition published by Gale Centre Publications 1992
Whitakers Way
Loughton Essex
IG10 1SQ

ISBN 1 870258 27 4

Designed and printed in Great Britain by Metloc Printers Limited, Loughton, Essex

Photographs are by Susan Pearson, Lavon Harrison, Sheila Christl and Derek Gale.
The photographs on the cover are by Sheila Christl (right) and Roger Jewel (left). They are the same person. The smaller one was taken after a time spent in a residential setting of poor quality; the main one shows her a year later, after being restored to the love and care provided by her daughter.

Tom Kitwood and Kathleen Bredin have produced an excellent guide for carers. Their work is based on a deep appreciation of human nature, including the human nature of those who suffer from dementia. Their belief in the value of people shines through their writing. It is a welcome antidote to the way in which our national life and even our health service have become obsessed by economic values. However, theirs is no mere philosophical analysis. It is intensely practical, based on their own extensive experience in evaluating quality of care for old people with dementia.

This book focusses on people with dementia and how to enhance their well-being. It deals with matters such as their need for company, for security and variety. The book stresses the importance of the individual history, characteristics and remaining abilities of people with dementia. Practical problems like wandering, incontinence and aggression are approached from a new angle, interpreting many accepted ways of helping in the light of respect for the individual. There is also a balanced consideration of the needs of carers, a section on the rights of those with dementia and a useful list of further sources of help.

It is heart-warming to read such a careful, practical account of how to help people with dementia. I hope you find the experience as rewarding as I did.

John P Wattis MB DPM FRCPsych
St James's University Hospital
Leeds

1

CONTENTS

PERSON TO PERSON

Nobody knows exactly why some people lose their mental powers. We do know that this is a huge problem, for it happens to about one person in ten among the over-seventies, and also to some at a much younger age. It involves a lot of suffering, both for the person who is affected and for others who are close. Not all of the suffering is due simply to brain damage and its effects. Some of the suffering comes about because we do not yet understand clearly how to provide the best kind of care. Medical science is a very long way from giving us any cures or preventatives, and it has not yet found ways of stopping a person from going downhill. The only solutions within our grasp are to be found at a simple, honest, human level; through kindness and understanding, and through love, where that is possible.

This book, then, is written mainly for two groups of people. The first group consists of wives, husbands, sons, daughters, sisters, brothers, in-laws - all family members who are looking after someone at home. The second group consists of those who are employed in caring work, or who have taken it on as a volunteer. Depending on which group you belong to, your aims and your needs will be rather different from those in the other group. Yet you need to understand one another, or you may need to later on. Some of the basic guidelines for good caring will be the same for you both.

If you are a family carer, this may be one of the most difficult, upsetting and exhausting periods of your whole life. You have a practical task in hand, one which requires great patience and skill. You may well be needing more support than you are actually getting, and perhaps you feel that not so many people understand what you are facing. Besides keeping up your daily routine, you are continually having to adjust to the changes that are going on. Your relationship with the person you are looking after is different now from what it used to be, and it will be different yet again. Perhaps you look back and long for the old days when everything seemed secure, yet you realise that those days will never come back. You are giving so much, but there are days when you feel that you are receiving so little in return. You have important decisions to make, but sometimes you just don't know what is the right thing to do. In the face of all this, you are still wanting to give of your best.

If you are one of the second group, your position as a careworker is different. You are doing this work as a job, whether for pay or as a volunteer. You are not so closely and painfully involved as family members. For some of you your career will be in one of the caring professions. For others this work may simply be something that you have taken on for a short while - or even because you can't find other paid employment. Whatever has brought you into caring work, you know that it will be much more satisfying if you are able to do it well.

We have written this book as a result of spending many hours in the company of people whose mental powers are failing. Also we have had many talks both with family members and professionals, trying to understand their successes and failures, their needs and problems. As part of our work we have been developing ways of testing out whether places such as residential homes and day centres are giving good quality care. All this has given us a clear picture of what works well and what works badly. All of the little stories in the book are based in some way on our experience. We wrote a first edition of the book, and had a lot of valuable comments on it, from family members and professionals. They have enabled us to improve it, and we are very grateful for their help. From the knowledge we have gained we are convinced that the full picture of why mental powers fail, and how care can be most effective, has not yet been painted. In and around these strange afflictions there can be a good deal of joy and satisfaction - far more than is commonly believed.

The basic message of the book is a very simple one. Those whose mental powers are failing or have failed need, in every way, to be treated as persons, just as we ourselves would like to be treated. In the following pages this message is spelled out in detail, applying it to our attitudes and approaches, and to many of the practical details of caring work. As you will see, there are no pat answers, no recipes for making all problems disappear. But the work of a carer can be full of meaning, and there is ground for hope.

The authors wish to express their thanks to:

The many family carers who gave us their time and attention, and shared their experience and wisdom with us

The staff and residents of Spring Mount and Lawrence House Residential Homes, and the staff and patients of Northern View Day Hospital, Bradford, who made us welcome on many occasions.

Davinder Kaur Singh and Margaret Wilkinson, who typed the manuscript with care and patience

The many readers who gave us their advice after seeing an earlier version of this book

Susan Pearson, Lavon Harrison, Sheila Christl, Derek Gale and Roger Jewel who took the photographs

The Leverhulme Trust, which provided the funding for the research programme during the course of which this book was written

And most of all, the men and women with failing mental powers who simply allowed us to be with them, and shared something of the meaning of their lives.

Tom Kitwood and Kathleen Bredin

LET'S FOCUS ON

THE WHOLE

PERSON

It can often help us to understand people better if we try to put ourselves in their shoes. So would you take some time to sit down quietly and set aside your everyday concerns? In your imagination picture yourself as someone whose mental powers are failing.

How would it be? You might feel lonely, even when there are lots of people nearby. You might feel insecure, or powerless, or very frightened.

Sometimes you might feel frustrated or angry. People seem to treat you differently, sometimes like an idiot, sometimes like a child, at other times like an object. You might even wonder whether you are still a person at all. How would you want others to treat you?

You would still have the same desires as before. You'd have the same need for company, but you might feel it more urgently because your handicaps made you feel so alone. You'd want people to be kind and generous, not judging or criticizing you. You'd want them to slow down to your pace. You'd want them to try to understand your language, because you had such difficulties with theirs.

You'd need to know that you still mattered, and that you'd never be deprived of their loving care. You would want to remain, in every sense, a member of the human race.

This picture tells us a bit about what it's like to be someone whose mental powers are failing. We care best when we remember that each individual is a person and needs to be treated as such in order to be all that they can be. You yourself are not just a dutiful family member, an employee or a volunteer. You are a person; and the one you give care to is not just a patient or a disabled being, but a person as well. Just as you need to be treated as a person by others in order to feel good about yourself, they do too. You need to be heard, to be understood; they do too. You need to know that some others genuinely care for you; they do too. Each one of us is unique, special, with our own history, our family, our group of friends, our personal strengths and weaknesses, our hang-ups, our pains. We have all these things in common, no matter how great our abilities or disabilities. These are what make human beings into PERSONS.

Whether we fare well or badly as persons depends on whether our needs and abilities are recognized - by ourselves and by others. It depends too, on how much those others are willing to support and encourage us. The same is true for those whose mental powers are failing.

WHAT MEDICAL SCIENCE CAN TELL US

Some years ago, people who became severely confused in later life, and who never got better, were said to have 'gone senile'. We still hear that kind of talk sometimes today. It doesn't help, because it sets confused people apart from everyone else. It even suggests that they aren't fully human any more, and that almost nothing can be done for them as persons. How far that is from the truth.

Medical research has shown that people can become confused because of various causes. Some of these can be treated, or even cured completely.

- There may be an infection, such as pneumonia
- The body chemistry may be out of balance

- The person may be suffering from depression
- Important foodstuffs may be lacking from the diet
- Drugs might be building up in the body, or causing side effects

There are other causes, too, which doctors can deal with. If someone does show signs of confusion, it is important that possible causes such as these are investigated. The key thing is to make sure that all proper tests are carried out, while protecting the person from 'assessments' that are pointless and discouraging.

But there are some kinds of confusion that are permanent, and which tend to become more severe as time goes on. These conditions can occur at any age, but they are far more common among people in their seventies and eighties. Often they are given the label 'dementia'; but the term isn't really helpful, because it conjures up a picture of someone who is out of their mind or raving. As with the idea of 'going senile', it tends to create an 'us' and a 'them'. Try thinking instead of those who suffer in this way simply as persons, some of whose mental powers are failing. This disability is linked to faulty working or permanent damage in the brain.

When Florence was first seen by her G.P. she seemed to be very confused. She was referred to a consultant, and she began to attend the day hospital. It became clear that she was severely depressed, and that she had not been eating well for some time. Her diet was improved, her depression was treated medically, and a volunteer began to visit her regularly at home. All her confusion disappeared.

9

Medical science tells us that the damage to the brain is of two main kinds. The more common kind involves the destruction of brain cells because of causes that are not well understood. Although there may be several types of this general disorder, they are usually known today as Alzheimer's Disease. Much research is being carried out to try to find the cause or causes. There are several possibilities, such as low levels of certain brain chemicals (called neurotransmitters), exposure to aluminium or other metals, a slow-acting virus, or the after-effects of head injury. However, there is not yet any clear evidence of a cause or a cure.

The other type of damage to the brain, which is rather less common, occurs because of failure of the blood supply to brain cells. In some instances it is rather as if the person has had a series of tiny strokes. The brains of some severely confused people are probably damaged in both types of way.

It is widely believed that once a person has developed one of these illnesses, he or she is bound to go downhill, and perhaps end up with no human powers at all. Nowadays this idea is being questioned, as we learn more about good caring. People are known to stop deteriorating, or even improve in certain ways, when the care is of a kind that really suits them. Some of the changes, though, can never be reversed. The main point is that however far an individual's brain has failed, and for whatever reason, he or she is still a person, and needs to be treated as one.

WHAT CAN BE DONE?

If we look at people with 'dementia' mainly in terms of what has gone wrong, and of powers they have lost, we may come to feel that there is nothing we can do that will be of really positive help. We might come to see them mainly as patients with a fatal illness. Professional careworkers who have this attitude then tend to see their highest goal as meeting the confused person's basic needs - for food and drink, for cleanliness, for toileting, for warmth, comfort and rest - and nothing more. So it is easy to fasten onto the idea of 'dementia' and the facts about the damage to the brain and say that nothing more can be done. Really this is a kind of despair. It's still common, but it isn't justified.

So far as is known at present, very little can be done by medical means to slow down or stop the destruction of brain cells, and certainly there is no way of bringing back to life cells that have died. As carers we need to accept that there is much that we can't do. But a great deal can be done if we are able to keep in contact at the human level, person-to-person.

The mental powers that fail are generally those to do with thought and memory, while feelings and sociability need not be so seriously affected. With help and support, a confused person can remain in a state of well-being to a far greater extent than many people believe. Of course, he or she will experience distress at times; but then, that's true of all of us, isn't it?

You, the carer, will have many needs, and we will be looking at these in Chapter 13 (page 81). If you are a family member there may be a process of grieving to go through, and this will be discussed in Chapter 14 (page 89). But before we come to these things, let's try to understand more deeply what it is like to be someone whose mental powers are failing, and what is involved in person-to-person care.

EACH PERSON
IS SPECIAL

No two people are exactly alike, not even identical twins. Each one of us has our own personality, life history, place in the world. We like to feel ourselves as distinct, as well as feeling connected to others. If we have an illness or a disability, it does not take away from our uniqueness. No-one should be lumped together with others under some general label. However handicapped or disabled, each person is still an individual. When people's mental powers are failing, it is doubly important to recognize this to help them preserve their sense of identity. Sensitive family carers know that this is vital. Also the best care schemes try to plan what they do by taking each person's needs into account.

THE PAST IN THE PRESENT

As we go on through life we build up a personal history, with its unique mix of joys and pleasures, sorrows and pains. Our sense of who we are is linked to that history, and if we lose that we also lose something of ourselves. This is important for all people, whatever their age. If a person's mental powers begin to fail, he or she will be unable to do some of the things that were possible before. Some parts of life, like having a job, or visiting a wide circle of friends, or travelling around, may now be over, so personal history becomes all the more important. Often people who become confused about the present still have quite a good memory for the more distant past; it is one of their great assets, if others will help them to use it. Photographs, clothes and treasured possessions can all be of value here.

One small warning. For some people the past is full of painful memories, and they may not want to be reminded of it. Try to sense whether or not it would be helpful to go back into the past, and see if the person you are caring for would welcome you as their companion 'down memory lane'.

▲ For Careworkers

It is a good idea if you can get to know as much as possible about the life story of each of the people you are helping to look after. Think for a moment; what do you actually know about each one? How many of the following questions could you answer?

- *What is their family background?*

- *What do you know about their husband or wife, brothers and sisters, children, grandchildren and even great-grandchildren?*

- *What type of work did they do before retirement?*

- *Who have been the significant people in their lives?*

- *Who are the important people in their lives at present?*

- *What are their personal likes and dislikes?*

- *What have they been proud of in their lives?*

- *What do they value?*

- *How have they spent their leisure time?*

- *Do they have religious beliefs, or connections with any religious grouping?*

- *What are their past and present interests?*

- *Were they ever involved in politics?*

- *What major illnesses have they had? Have they ever been in hospital?*

- *How has their health been recently?*

- *What happened to their home situation in the months before you got to know them?*

- *How have they coped with difficulties in the past?*

- *How are their family members coping with what is happening now?*

If you don't know, could you make the effort to find out answers to at least some of these questions? Probably there's a great deal that the people in your care can tell you themselves, if you will give them the time. Some of them will value the chance to talk about themselves to a person who listens with real attention and interest. There may also be records that you can look at. Perhaps you will be able to add to these from what you find out. Have you considered keeping a small record book yourself? You can talk with family members when they visit, or make contact with them some other way. (You might need to do this via your supervisor, or at least with their permission). Generally family members are eager to give information about their relative, for they know that it will lead to a more personal form of care.

■ For Family Carers

If your relative is attending a day care centre, or goes from time to time into respite care, or is now being looked after in a residential or nursing home, could you help to make the care more personal? Have you passed on as much information as you would like? Is there any really painful bit of the past that care staff should know about, so as to avoid a tactless blunder? Are you able to meet with any of them and tell them more?

A NOTE ON NAMES

Our sense of who we are is closely linked to our name. Have you ever been called by the wrong name, and noticed how upsetting it can be? It feels as if something about us has been denied, or ignored, or taken away. So if caregiving is to be truly personal, it is necessary to respect each person's wishes about their name. We don't want to add to the confusion by implying that they are someone else. If your relative is receiving formal care, part-time or full-time, check that the name he or she is being called by is one that seems to feel right. Many carers automatically assume that they can use first names or begin to use nicknames. Although many of those with failing mental powers do seem to accept this, it would be better if the staff actually asked permission. Some may wish to be called Mr or Mrs by everyone except close family, and this should be respected. Serious misunderstandings can occur around the question of people's names.

WHOSE REALITY?

Each one of us sees, hears, feels, understands the world around us in our own special way. Each will respond to it in a way that is uniquely our own.

Imagine three people, all taking the same bus ride. The first is looking at the cars, eagerly watching out for any new models that he hasn't seen before. He hardly notices anything else. The second is busy admiring the gardens, and thinking about ways of brightening up her own. The third hasn't been on this journey before, and is anxiously looking out for a pub called 'The Craven Heifer', knowing that she has to get off at the first stop after that.

Each of the three was living in his or her own private 'reality'; for each of them certain things were important and others weren't. This idea applies not just to small things like bus journeys, but to big things too; such as religion, getting married, having children, growing old, being bereaved.

Many misunderstandings and conflicts come about because people forget this simple point. Instead they assume that another person shares their 'reality'; and if they don't, then they certainly ought to!

If two people live in different 'realities', how are they going to find agreement? It's not going to come if each one tries to force the other to see the world differently. But it might happen if each tries to understand the other's 'reality', and see that it, too, makes sense.

All this applies to the care of someone whose mental powers are failing. That person, too, has his or her own 'reality', and it may be a good deal different from our own. It's best to try to 'get inside' it, to have a sense of what it's like to be that person. And it's pointless to argue or quarrel about what we think are 'the facts'.

Those who are confused (as we judge it, from our 'reality') may make mistakes about who other people are. At times we will need to correct them, but not always. There may be some important meaning in the 'mistakes' that they are making.

A TRULY PERSONAL APPROACH TO CARE

When we really appreciate that each person is special, a new window is opened on the task of caring. We see how vital it is to take account of the unique desires, tastes, abilities, difficulties and fears of the one we are looking after. And we need to remember that any or all of these things may change as time goes on. It isn't easy, of course, and there have to be compromises. There are many things we simply have to get done, in order to carry on from day to day.

Family carers can easily miss this point, simply because they think they know the confused person so well. So it's necessary to keep an open mind. Any day may bring something new. Just because things have been a certain way in the past, it doesn't mean they're bound to be like that in the future.

Right from the time that he entered the nursing home Ron seemed to believe that the Manager, Sarah, was one of his relatives. Some days she was his daughter, some days his sister, some days his mother. Sarah didn't try to straighten him out on the facts. She took it rather that Ron felt as if she was one of his family, and that he expected warmth and kindness from her. She saw that there was a truth in what he was saying, a kind of poetic truth, and she took it as a compliment.

Professional carers, too, may find that they lose track of the individuality of some of those they are looking after. Sometimes staffing levels are low, and there are many routine jobs to attend to. It's certainly possible to treat each person as an individual, no matter how many people are involved. The best care schemes definitely do this. One mark of a poor scheme is that it doesn't really try; it simply lumps people together, and deals with them as a group. The real task of caring is not that of adapting individuals to one routine. Rather, the task is to adapt the routine as far as possible so as to meet the needs of each individual person. Later in the book we'll look at some ideas about how this can be done.

There's one main idea to get hold of at this point. Each person in the world has his or her own 'reality'. This is true for every individual whose mental powers are failing. To be effective carers we need to accept and respect the 'reality' of the one we are looking after. When we respond to that, rather than our own ready-made views about what's best, new life and hope are born.

CHAPTER 3

WHAT WE DO
AND HOW
WE DO IT

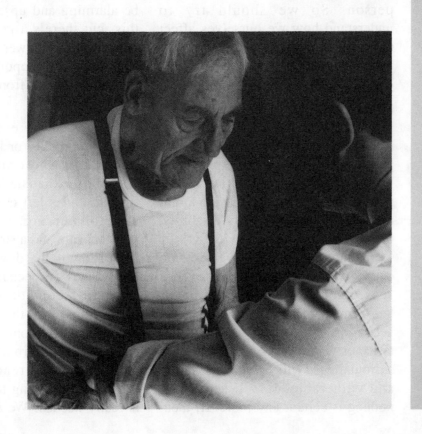

Good care does not simply rest on good intentions, general kindness and common sense. These things are important, but not enough. Persons whose mental powers are failing need you to develop a 'special sense', based on understanding their 'reality'. They need you to see past their disability and find their strengths. They need you to treat them, not as 'Alzheimer victims', but as fully human beings. They need you to make real contact, person-to-person. So we should try to understand how we ourselves affect those whom we are looking after, and how they affect us as well.

The loss of brain cells may bring about a decline of an individual's mental powers, but it is the failure of others to treat an individual with proper attention and respect that brings about the destruction of the person. Does this mean that we might actually add to someone's disability, or even contribute to their 'dementia', through the ways we do or do not treat them? The answer is yes. Anyone who senses that his or her memory is unreliable, or that it is becoming hard to carry out familiar tasks, or who has got lost in familiar surroundings, will be feeling fragile and vulnerable. It will seem that nothing is certain any more. If, then,

that person is treated in ways that are insensitive or uncaring, the feelings of insecurity will be greatly increased. We, ourselves, know that others can destroy our sense of well-being, and even lead us to be uncertain about who we are, if they do not treat us as real persons. Far more so is this true for those whose mental powers are failing, because they can be easily undermined at the very point where they are in need of extra support and reassurance. It may be alarming and upsetting to realise this, but there's a good side too. It lies within our power to reach out, to encourage, to support them, and so reduce the effects from damage to the brain.

Poor care hardly ever comes from deliberate cruelty or heartlessness. It can occur when we are overloaded or just plain exhausted. It may result from attitudes left over from the old style of nursing, where efficient physical care and a strict routine were the order of the day; the patients' other needs - especially their feelings - weren't considered important. Sometimes, too, the behaviour and difficulties of a confused person will challenge or disturb us. Then we may find ourselves reacting without thinking, and losing touch with what is really needed. We are only human after all, and we are learners. There are bound to be times when we aren't as sensitive or skilled as we would like to be. It is best to forgive ourselves our failings, accept that we're not perfect, and learn to do better. The more we really understand how and why we sometimes 'take away' from a confused person, the more we may also discover how to 'give back .'

So here are some typical situations, followed by examples of bad and good care practice. They are not meant as a list of do's and don'ts. They are simply meant to show ways in which a person whose mental powers are failing can be further injured or weakened by bad practice; or how, through good practice, they can be valued and restored.

BAD PRACTICE

GOOD PRACTICE

Elsie's husband is leaving after his visit to the residential home. He gives her a big warm hug as he goes, but she becomes distressed afterwards.

A carer notices her distress and says cheerfully, 'He's just gone out for a short time, love. He'll be back soon. Now, Elsie, come to the table and have your tea.'

The carer says to her affectionately, 'I know you miss him but he will be back to visit you on Tuesday. I'll give you a big hug each day until he comes back. Now, shall we go and mark Tuesday on your bedside calendar so you'll know which day he is coming back?'

Mr Evans is struggling to eat his dessert. He is managing, although slowly, as it often slips off the spoon. He is the last person still seated at his table.

The carer gets impatient, takes his spoon from him, and feeds him the rest of his dessert.

The carer assures him that it is alright to take his time so he can enjoy his dessert. Next time, she arranges the table seating so that Mr Evans can be with other slow eaters, and not feel pressured.

Albert, aged 89, had recently gone into a nursing home. The routine here included giving baths twice a week. Albert became violent when staff tried to give him a bath. No amount of coaxing would help. A nurse rang up Albert's wife and found that he had taken baths only on Sundays for nearly all of his life. The nurse decided there was no need to alter his pattern now. The next Sunday the staff made it clear that it really was Sunday, and he happily took his bath.

It was a carers' support group meeting. Several of the members of the group shared the problems they were having because the one they were looking after was aggressive and difficult. Together they came to the conclusion that they were exerting far too much control, and were not allowing their relative to make any decisions. So they explored together some of the ways in which their relative could be safely allowed to have choices and experience more freedom.

Dorothy has had an accident and messed herself. No one was around to get her to the toilet in time.

The carer announces 'Oh, Dorothy, what have you done? We'll have to get you in nappies soon, won't we?'

Kindly and discreetly, the carer helps her to the toilet to clean up. She shows Dorothy that she is not shocked or critical. After Dorothy feels less upset, they chat about other things.

Michael is causing trouble by continually taking food off other people's plates

A carer says to him 'Now, Michael, if you carry on doing this we'll have to send you away from here. Then you'll have no place to live.'

A carer notices that directing Michael to his own plate doesn't help because he is too restless to sit through a meal, even though hungry. She tries making Michael's meal into a sandwich, so that he can eat it as he walks about.

A visitor and a carer are talking about Lily, who is nearby.

The carer says to the visitor, 'We can't do much with Lily now. She is very advanced in the disease and isn't able to settle down to anything.'

The carer introduces the visitor to Lily and gives Lily a compliment, directly: 'Lily, you seem very bright and busy today,' The visitor then joins in the conversation.

Hilda keeps calling out 'I want to go home, I want to go home!'

A carer says accusingly, 'You can't go home, Hilda, because you burnt your house down.'

The carer realises Hilda may be feeling lost and not a part of things. He invites Hilda to a quiet sitting area and sensitively re-introduces her to Joe, another resident. The carer stays a few minutes to help them get to know each other .

It is teatime and Caroline is watching the television. Her carer is trying to find out what she is wanting.

He says to her, as he swiftly moves across the room: 'Do you want to finish watching your show or do you want to have your tea? I've made your favourite pie, and it's good and hot now, but it will cool off if you don't hurry. Your show is almost over, so what do you want to do?' He waits for a moment as Caroline looks up, completely bewildered, then walks into the kitchen mumbling sadly, 'I might as well talk to myself.'

The carer turns down the TV and kneels down in front of Caroline, 'I've made your favourite pie.' She responds with a smile. He says, 'Do you want to eat now?' Caroline nods yes, and then follows him through to the kitchen.

Eddie has tried to stroke the legs of a careworker

She turns to him, with an expression of disgust and says, 'How dare you? I'm certainly not speaking to you any more today!' She turns her back on him and walks away.

She says to him seriously, but not in a scolding manner, 'Eddie, I don't like it when you do that. I like you, Eddie, but I don't want you to do that any more.'

Mr MacDonald looks very angry. He hammers his fist down on the table. No-one pays any attention. Then he puts his head in his hands, and looks sad and bewildered.

The carer comes close to him and says, cheerfully, 'Now, Angus, I'm sure it's going to be a lovely day. I've brought you a nice cup of tea.'

The carer sits down beside him. 'Mr MacDonald, you look troubled. I'll stay with you for a while.' She waits, quietly, in his company. Then throughout the day she remains aware of how he had been feeling.

Mr. Cook was a very 'respectable' man. He was looking after his mother, aged 87. She was losing some of her neat and tidy ways, and sometimes insisted on wearing dirty clothes. Often he would be very critical of her, and she seemed hurt and angry. He then began to change his attitude. He started to praise her when she looked nice, and slowly became less critical. As he did this, her dress and appearance improved just a little. Their relationship however, became much more gentle and accepting.

Ada is asleep in a chair. The carer needs to plug an appliance into the wall socket, but Ada's chair is in the way.

Without saying a word, the carer drags Ada's chair, with Ada in it, out of the way. Ada wakes up startled, but the carer just walks away.

The carer gently wakes up Ada, 'Sorry to wake you Ada, but I'm needing to get behind your chair. Is it alright if I move your chair a bit?' When Ada is ready, the carer gently moves the chair aside, talking with her at the same time.

These examples show twelve different kinds of situation. They illustrate bad practice, and also what might be done instead. If we go over the examples again, we can make a list of the things that might make matters worse for someone who is seriously and permanently confused.

-Using tricks or lies.
-Doing things for a person which they are actually able to do for themselves.
-Treating a person as if they had the abilities or experience of a very young child.
-Using power or threats which cause anxiety or fear.
-Giving a person a label which says that they are not a proper human being.
-Accusing a person, or throwing back in their face something they did or didn't do.
-Failing to slow down conversation, or to make it simple, so that real understanding can occur.

-Excluding a person from our company, or sending them away, because they have done something we don't approve of.
-Ignoring a person's feelings, or not taking them seriously.
-Treating a person like a lump of matter, or an animal, rather than as a living, feeling, human being.

When things like this happen, something important is 'taken away'. Also, a person is likely to feel discouraged and hopeless if he or she has to spend many hours without real human contact. This happens to some who are living alone, and can also occur in poorly run care settings. It's clear, then, that 'dementia' isn't just the result of damage to the brain. Human insensitivity and human neglect can add to someone's confusion. Personal care and attention can make up for much of what is lacking.

CHAPTER 4

COMPANY AND
CONTACT

For all of her life, Mrs Grant had never been very sociable. People tended to reach out to her, but never the reverse. She and her husband had few outside interests, and after the children were grown up their life was a private one, centred on their home. After Mr Grant died, the children encouraged their mother to take up hobbies and to make new friends. She said she wasn't interested, but actually she lacked the confidence. Her increasing memory problems made her even more anxious about making contact with others. Her lifestyle remained the same, but without her constant companion, it wasn't the same at all to her.

We are designed to be sociable. When human life began it involved groups of people who shared a great deal together, and were in close contact with each other most of the time. Today people move around more, and many live farther apart from families and friends, but our basic nature has remained unchanged. We tend to feel good about ourselves, and about life, when there are some others we can be close to, and whom we can trust. We want to share our feelings and experiences, and to know that we are understood and accepted, just as we are. All this is true for those who are in later life. Many older people crave for more company and more human contact.

Those whose mental powers are failing need company and contact, perhaps more so than others. Thus it is important to recognize and promote their social nature, and to do all we can to enable them to make and maintain a life shared with others. Sociability is a strength that can continue and blossom, even while other abilities are in decline. Some men and women who were shy and uneasy in company may become much more open and friendly when their memories are failing; perhaps they don't feel the need to hold themselves back so much as before. One clear sign that a person is faring well despite suffering from 'dementia' is being socially confident and at ease.

RESPOND TO FEELINGS

The heart is more powerful than the head. Our feelings are deeper than our thoughts. So far as is known, those parts of the brain which deal with feelings are much less likely to be damaged than the parts that deal with thoughts. Carers, then, need to be specially sensitive to the feelings of those whom they are looking after.

Feelings cover a wide range. It is easy perhaps, to respond to a sense of pleasure, happiness or hope in others. But we need to be able to respond to all kinds of feelings, including those which might seem to be negative. Often it is a mistake to try to cheer up someone who is downcast; we may simply be trying to keep ourselves from being downcast too. Feelings of anger, resentment, envy, frustration, sadness and despair are part of every person's life. If we do not accept these feelings and allow others to express them, we are giving them the message that we do not take these feelings seriously, that the feelings are not real. And this is not far from telling them that we are not taking them seriously, or that they are not real persons.

Remember that many people in later life will have lost a great deal. Probably friends or loved ones will have died recently. Some will never really have recovered from losing their job or trade, or their role as a parent or homemaker. There are losses of health, energy, and opportunities for an active sexual life. For most people there is a loss of income and the security that goes with it. Some people, despite such losses, are able to cope quite well and find contentment. But for others the losses tend to pile up onto each other, causing anxiety and stress. Those whose mental powers are failing have yet another kind of loss to cope with. It's a loss that could threaten their sense of who they are. For a while they may try to hide the fact from themselves or from others. If we bear in mind that this is what they face, we will find that making contact is easier. When we can respond to the sense of loss, we will be able to respond to many other feelings too.

People who develop Alzheimer's Disease at an earlier age may have had fewer losses in their past. But now they are having to face the fact that many of their former hopes and ambitions have been destroyed. Like those who are older, they are urgently in need of support and love.

BECOMING AN INTERPRETER

We may need to develop special skills in order to understand what a confused person is trying to get across. This is true even if we have known them for a very long time. The best thing is to treat everything they say, however jumbled or fantastic it may seem to be, as an attempt to tell us something. In fact, you need to become a bit like an interpreter of a foreign language. There is one big difference, though; there are as many different languages as there are confused individuals. The key thing is not to get hung up on the literal meaning of the words. Look for the message that underlies the words, or a need that is being expressed. Get a sense of the feeling that is coming across with the words.

It's not always clear what a person is needing. We may have to guess.

Rose is in bed with her husband. Suddenly she sits up, looks at him and says 'Who are you?' She shows no sign of fear; it's not as if there's a burglar in her bed. Perhaps she needs reassurance. He says 'It's me, love, your husband Richard'. And he holds her hand affectionately.

Jack is wandering round the residential home continually calling out 'Where am I? Where am I?' What is he needing? Perhaps he is feeling insecure and abandoned, and would be helped if someone walked around with him for a while, arm in arm. Just giving him the fact that he is now in Riverside Residential Home probably wouldn't help at all.

A careworker is helping Mrs Ivy Jones to get dressed. 'Now, Ivy, here's a sock. Put it on this foot . . . Now put this sock on the other foot . . . Can you get your foot into this shoe? . . . that's right.' And so on.

Winnie has knocked over a cup of tea. A careworker comes up to her and scolds her. 'Now, Winnie, why did you spill your tea?' On another day Winnie does the same thing. This time the careworker says to her, gently and kindly, 'No need to worry. I'll just give it a quick wipe and you can get back to your chat with Mary'.

Try to get a sense of what people are saying with their bodies. What is the expression on their face? Are they making contact with their eyes? Do they seem to be tensed up in any way? Does any part of their body look as if it's wanting to move? If you can answer these questions you may have a pretty good idea of what they are feeling, even if they can't put it into words. What's more, many people whose brains are severely damaged may lose the ability to form words and sentences altogether. If so, their lifeline into the company of others will be your ability to get hold of what they are saying in other ways.

There is a well-known range of so-called 'problem behaviours', often found in those whose mental powers are failing (see page 42). Sometimes these can be understood simply as 'last ditch' attempts to make contact or to protest. If we ignore these efforts, those who are struggling to communicate may become depressed. Even worse, they may finally give up trying to be recognized as valuable, and withdraw into themselves. Perhaps this is really what's happening when it is said that a person has become like a vegetable.

If on the other hand, we do respond to these efforts at communication, we are helping to keep them in the world of real persons. We might not interpret their messages correctly every time; but even so we will have made contact, and real understanding can grow from this.

IMPROVE YOUR MESSAGE

Remember, communication goes both ways. Just as you may not always find it easy to understand what a confused person is saying, they may have problems in understanding you. It might be simply a matter of hearing, for many older people become slightly deaf. So be sure to speak clearly and slowly. If your voice tends to be light or squeaky, try making it deeper. If a person needs a hearing aid, make sure they have been fitted for one. Check that they are using it, and that it is turned on. Generally it is helpful if you are in front of a person when you speak, and fairly close, so that they can see your face and watch your lip movements. Also, you are likely to keep their attention more. Sometimes caregivers make the mistake of speaking too loud, or almost shouting. Of course you need to speak up, but don't overdo it.

Even if a person can hear you, they may find it hard to grasp what you are meaning. So choose simple words. Use short sentences. Find a clear way of saying what you want to say. If the person you are with doesn't understand, simply repeat what you said before. (If you use different words, this may add to their confusion). Remember that their minds may be working much more slowly than yours. They may need time to take things in. If you are helping someone and giving them instructions, break these up into very simple parts, allowing time for a response after each suggestion.

Perhaps most important of all, remember that a confused person will depend heavily on what you say without words. A hurried and exasperated tone of voice and sharp body movements will be heard as disapproval or impatience. A smile and genuine affection will give a message of reassurance and warmth. If you are relaxed in your body, you'll pass that message on in many subtle ways; the people you are with will be more able to relax as well.

In talking with a person whose mental powers are failing, try not to put them on the spot. They may not be able to give an answer, or they may feel embarrassed or guilty.

PHYSICAL CONTACT

Lots of people in our society are deprived of touch. Some have had very few hugs and kisses in the last month or year. Many older people, especially if they have been living on their own, have been deprived of body contact for a very long time, and this may have added to feelings of loneliness and depression. So, be generous in offering contact: holding a hand, or walking arm in arm, accepting or giving a kiss. A person may want to relax in contact with you, cuddled up like a child. Many people appreciate a little massage, especially round the shoulders. It relieves muscular tension, and it can be a way of giving and receiving touch without embarrassment.

Take care, though. Some people are not used to a lot of body contact, or even may fear it. Don't force contact onto anyone. Also each of us, as caregivers, has personal boundaries. It doesn't help anyone if we go beyond these, and then feel uneasy. So look for a way that both meets the other person's need and which is respectful to yourself.

Mrs Thornton had become quite anxious and restless. Her carers thought she needed more stimulation. So they tried many activities, but she would show interest for only a moment before walking away. Then they wondered if she needed more body contact. Mrs Thornton's day became different from this time forward. When walking she often had a companion, arm in arm; there were hand and back massages, hairbrushing sessions, and lots of spontaneous hugs and kisses in between. As time went on, everyone noticed how much more happy, content and relaxed she appeared.

29

THE SPICE
OF LIFE

We all need to be active in some way. We need to have the sense that we are making some kind of mark on the world. It's true of a baby; it's true of a severely handicapped person; it's true of healthy individuals who are in their prime; it's true of anyone, of whatever age, whose mental powers are failing.

Let's look at this in a bit more detail. What does being active do for us?

- It gives a sense of achievement

- It improves our feelings about ourselves, our self-esteem

- It provides natural contact with other people

- It increases trust and the ability to cooperate

- It encourages self-expression, pleasure, laughter

- It gives life a meaning

- It promotes health and physical well-being

In other words, being active is a big part of what makes human beings into persons. Most of us go on, day by day, just assuming that we are going to be active. We don't stop to ponder on what it would be like if all this were taken away. But think for a moment about the possibility of losing your active powers. Even worse, imagine how it would be if you had to spend each day pretty much like the one before, doing almost nothing, week after week. It would be existing, not living. If this continued for too long you might lose the sense of being a person.

So think all this through, with a mind to the needs of the one whom you are looking after. Are they as active as they might be, or could be? The more activity you can help provide, the better they will feel and the more interesting your task will be.

TWO MISUNDERSTANDINGS

Sometimes confused people are kept from being as active as they might be, and one (or both) of two reasons are given. The first is that they need exactly the same routine day after day in order to feel secure. There's a grain of truth here. But the real point is that security comes first and foremost from trust in others who care, and from the sense that they are going to be around. It also comes from having a kind of base - a place that is really home. If these things are there, many confused people thrive on variety and change.

The other misunderstanding comes from assuming that confused people can do very little, and that the damage to their brains is going to take away almost all their abilities in due course. Again, there's a bit of truth here. But the real point is that there's a lot that they can do. Our skill is to find this out and work with it. If we don't help them to use the powers that they do have, these powers will go far more quickly than any advance in damage to the brain. There's a well-known saying 'If you don't use it, you lose it'. It's sobering to remember that an 80-year old with full mental powers who remains bedridden for as little as two or three months may never be able to walk independently again.

ADAPTED OPPORTUNITIES

Of course it's true that people with memory failure and other impairments can't do many of the things that they were able to do before. Sometimes, too, they seem to have lost interest. Maybe they feel disheartened at having to face the facts about their disabilities. But what we can do as caregivers is to provide 'adapted opportunities'. This means, ways of taking part in an activity that has been made more simple so as to take into account what they can and cannot do. When we take this idea seriously, we will often find that there's far more scope for activities than we had realised. Our task is to recognize and draw on the abilities that people do have, and then to fill in the bits that they can't do. This makes a kind of partnership, where each contributes something valuable. So keep on the look-out for ways of creating these adapted opportunities.

In Ethel's case for example, a simple household chore was taken and made into something of great value. It became a chance for Ethel to be really active, not just a passenger, and she knew that what she had done was appreciated.

People who are severely confused and frail will require less stimulation and challenge, and they will need more one-to-one attention. However, we can still try to offer enjoyable activities which are within their grasp, and which will have meaning for them.

A FEW SUGGESTIONS ABOUT THINGS TO DO

It may be helpful to make a list of all the things you might possibly be able to do with the person in your care. There could be many more than you realise. It might help if you talked this over with one or two others.

A guiding principle is to give enough to challenge and add variety, but not so much that a person becomes

Ethel has a severe memory problem, but she's always bustling around, trying to be helpful. The carer asks her if she could give a hand by wiping down the table after lunch. She stays with Ethel, doing the same job too. She thanks her at the end, and Ethel looks very pleased. A little more wiping needs to be done later, but that doesn't matter.

Three others have just picked a lovely assortment of flowers from the garden. Mrs Murphy, who is immobile and very confused, couldn't do this with them. Now it is time to arrange the flowers, and Mrs Murphy is invited to be in charge. The flowers are spread out on a tray on her lap. She selects them one by one, enjoying the scent of each, and a carer places them in a vase.

Mrs. Goldman had been a very good cook during her married days, and had greatly enjoyed catering for her family. Now at age 94, she was looked after by her youngest son Ben, aged 67. Often she seemed to be bored and disinterested. One day Ben decided to ask her to help him make a fruitcake, in preparation for a visit from her grandchildren. They sat together in the kitchen and Ben gave her tasks that she could do. She began to sing, as she used to do in the kitchen when her family was young. The cake was a great success.

frustrated or exhausted. Here are a few ideas; but of course the list will be unique to each person, according to their abilities and tastes.

Cooking There's much here that even a very confused person can do: putting measured ingredients into a bowl, mixing, kneading, cutting out pastry, and so on. Smelling, tasting and showing off the finished product can be enjoyed by almost everyone. Remember that some men like cooking, too, even though not all will want to.

Dancing Many people keep their know-how at dancing, even when they are very confused. It's one of the best activities, because it's done with others, it's fun, and it's skilled. Any kind of movement to music, even if it's just with arms or hands, is a kind of dance. So someone who is no longer able to walk can still take part.

Flowers Flowers can give pleasure in many ways. Just seeing them, ready arranged, is one of the least of these. Confused people might pick some flowers, arrange them in a vase, smell them, feel the petals; and someone who is fully safe with secateurs might even do a bit of dead-heading.

Games What a long list of things might be included here: table games like dominoes or skittles, ball games like pool or bowls, card games, bingo, arm-wrestling - even charades. Just remember the bit about adapted opportunities; many more partnerships will be required.

Gardening Lots of garden jobs could be adapted so that a person whose mental powers are failing can at least give a hand. What about mowing, or raking up leaves, or preparing ground for sowing? Some younger people with Alzheimer's Disease will have a lot of strength, and may even enjoy heavy digging. Almost anything is possible provided that it's safe, and that it doesn't involve tricky 'judgments' (e.g. between seedlings and weeds, or between fruit that's ready for picking and fruit that's not yet ripe). And then there's a lot that can be done with houseplants too: re-potting, taking and planting cuttings, growing something from seed.

Housework It's commonly thought that confused people want to be totally looked after. Often the truth is that they want to make a contribution, to feel needed and useful. So what about giving a chance for someone to do a bit of dusting, or hoovering, or windowcleaning? Make sure it's safe for them to do, and that precious items won't get broken.

Music Just as with dancing, abilities and memories here often remain long after memory for recent events has gone. If you are a family carer you know the favourite tunes, or favourite types of music, for the person you are looking after. If you are a careworker, try to find out. You could try a singalong, whether it is just the two of you or twenty. You could use simple instruments, or whatever would do instead, to make a band.

Outings It is pleasant to get away and be in some other place for a while - provided the company is right! There's going into the country, or having a picnic, or going for a ride on a steam train. Closer to home there's the pub or the park. If it's a place you don't know, it may be helpful to you to check it out in advance, to see if there are sufficient chairs, shelter, or obstacles such as stairs, etc.

Pets Many people who are severely confused like pets very much, and often the pets seem to realise it too. You can be close to a pet, make contact with them, without having to talk 'sense'. You don't have to talk at all!

Religious Observance Did the person in your care have any kind of spiritual faith? And if so, are they being given the opportunity now to continue to practice it? People who have been believers for many years have a faith that is built into their whole way of life. Words of hymns and prayers may still be recalled long after other speech has been forgotten.

Walks Going for a walk doesn't have to be somewhere special; even a simple, familiar walk in the neighbourhood can make a good change from being indoors. It's exercise, and it's a reminder of the local area. But walks further afield can be wonderful, too. Some people don't take to 'walking for walking's sake'. There are lots of ways to fit a walk in with something else, such as going to a shop or the post office, or going over to a cafe for a cup of tea. Best of all, perhaps, if there's a friend who really understands what's happening, how about walking round to say hello?

BE GENEROUS WITH PRAISE

Those whose mental powers are failing have so many difficulties and disadvantages, they need all the praise and encouragement they can get. So be ready to give 'pats on the back' when something has gone well.

Mrs. O'Shaughnessey had been a very devout member of her church throughout her life and she had attended Mass daily. When she was first admitted to Broadstone Residential Home no one considered the fact that she might have spiritual needs. Some members of the St. Columba's congregation visited one day and gave her a tape recording they had made of some of the old Mass music. Staff began to play it for her each morning. Sometimes Mrs. O'Shaughnessey would sing with the music, and it seemed to give her great satisfaction.

It's a game of bingo. Mike, a new careworker, is partnering Mr Dixon. As the game goes on Mike becomes more and more involved, almost as if Mr Dixon isn't there at all. In the end Mike stands up, shouts 'Bingo', smiles at everyone and says 'I've won'.

Lois is in a wheel chair, and she can get about in it. She's trying to move it, but it has got stuck against a sofa. Her carer speaks with her, frees the wheel chair, but doesn't push it anywhere. Lois moves on, and gets stuck in the doorway. The carer again asks if she'd like help, and guides her through the doorway. Lois seems to be wanting to go to the bedroom. The carer didn't just assume this, and push Lois there, quickly and efficiently. Lois was enabled to do what she wanted, in her own way.

■ For Family Carers

Do you sometimes forget this, especially when you are tired or upset? Keep your eyes open for when something goes well, however small. It might be as simple as putting on a pullover, or managing a visit to the toilet successfully. Welcome your relative warmly on return, if he or she goes to a day care centre.

▲ For Careworkers

You can sometimes do a great deal to encourage people in group settings. If you are skilled, you can use these occasions to spread good feelings around. Here are a few ideas:-

-a hug or handshake from everyone in the room -a chorus of 'for he's (or more likely, she's) a jolly good fellow' -a round of applause -three cheers -a badge, or a flower from the garden.

If you do do something like this, though, be careful that what you do for one person doesn't make others even more discouraged. Watch for every person's achievements, according to the abilities they do possess.

WHAT TO AVOID

As caregivers we're bound to make many mistakes. We are only human, after all. But it's worth mentioning three points about setting up activities.

First, avoid placing a person in your care in a situation where they are bound to fail. Probably they are already feeling very sensitive about what they can't do, and they don't need another painful reminder.

Second, avoid activities that involve too much abstract thought; usually this is where confused people are at their weakest.

Third, avoid setting things up so that you or another carer is really the active one, while the person you are caring for is either a spectator or doing something really trivial.

CARING IS CO-OPERATION

If you are all the time doing things for a person, while they are doing almost nothing, it won't be good for either of you. You will tend to become burdened and resentful; they will perhaps feel useless or just turn off altogether. It's far better if you learn how to fit your actions in together: giving and receiving, both ways.

The best caring is always a kind of co-operation, even when a person has very few abilities remaining. Although things may be extremely difficult, the kind of contact that this brings may help you both to feel that life is still worth living.

CHAPTER 6

A PLACE TO FEEL GOOD IN

Mrs Green's husband was determined to look after her at home. He obtained information from the Alzheimer's Disease Society, and he understood clearly what might be involved. For a while they managed with the small bathroom-lavatory, up a steep flight of stairs. Later this became very difficult. Mr Green took advice from Social Services, and a toilet was installed downstairs. He often left the door slightly open, so that the toilet could be seen. Also a shower was fitted upstairs in what had been a small bedroom. The shower had a seat. Mr Green wasn't very skilled at making the home look nice, but a Home Care Assistant came in twice a week, and helped in many different ways.

These changes made a huge difference to the life Mr and Mrs Green shared together.

It is important for any person that they like the place they live in. We want our own home to feel like home. This is especially true for those whose mental powers are failing, because they are going to be out and about far less than before. Also, people who have lost their memory for detail often seem still to have a very strong sense of place. So, as a carer, learn to be aware of how a place feels; and when it is in your power to do so, adapt it so as to meet the needs of the person you are looking after. If you haven't had much experience of looking after a home, you may be surprised at how much you learn to do.

■ For Family Carers

When you are caring for a confused person at home, some alterations may be required. You can get help and advice about this through Social Services or via your doctor. It may be necessary to make changes to the bathroom and toilet, or to the stairs. You might need extra covers for chairs and the bed. Parts of the kitchen layout may need to be altered, so as to avoid accidents. If you haven't been in the house together for very long, the one you are looking after may tend to get lost. Signposts or labels might be of use.

(If you do try this, observe carefully whether they really help; they do tend to make the house look strange, and a confused person's ability to use signs may be very limited anyway). Some of the changes your home requires just need commonsense. But expert advice is available, and you are entitled to it. Also you may be able to get financial help for the larger alterations.

▲ For Careworkers

Depending on the position you hold, you may or may not feel that you can bring about changes in the place where you work. However, when you notice that some arrangement isn't ideal, and you have suggestions about how it can be improved, why not try? At least you can bring it to the attention of those who can do something about it. If they are approached tactfully, and it's clear that you want to help make things better, you may find that your suggestions are really appreciated.

Consider the following checklist, which applies mainly to settings where care is given to a number of people. If you are a Home Care Assistant, though, much of it applies to the homes that you visit.

-**Temperature.** *Is it warm enough? Is it too hot? Are there any draughty places?*

-**Lighting.** *Is there enough light? Does anything cause dazzle? Can the lighting level be varied?*

-**Safety.** *Is there anything that could cause an accident? An unguarded fire? An over-hot radiator? A cable that might be tripped over?*

-**Furniture.** *Does it meet the range of needs, e.g. for eating at a table and for sitting comfortably? Is there anything that might tip over easily?*

-**Ventilation.** *Is there a through-put of air at any time? Do smells stay around, or can they be got rid of easily?*

-**Comfort.** *Are the main chairs really comfortable to sit in? Do they give sufficient back support? How easy are they to get in and out of? If an individual has a tendency to lie back straight, or lean to one side, are appropriate seats available? Are there any foot-rests and are they being used as needed?*

-**The toilet.** *Is it clearly marked and easy to get to? Does the person you are looking after know how to find it? Is it simple to use?*

-**Stimulation.** *What impression does the environment make on the eyes and ears? Is it homelike? Is there plenty to cause interest? Is it too much going on? Is the place boring or dull?*

-**Television.** *How is it being used? Having it on is fine if people are actually watching it, but constant television can easily distract attention while adding nothing. One mark of poor quality care, whether at home or in an institution, is that the television is left on as a substitute for human presence.*

-**Background music.** *How much is there, and of what kind? Music can be wonderfully soothing and relaxing. When combined with singing and dancing it can be one of the greatest sources of pleasure for confused people, whatever their age. But as with television, background music does not, in itself, bring stimulation. It won't fill the gap that can only be filled by real human contact.*

-**Bedrooms.** *As you walk into one of these, does it immediately reflect something of the occupant, or could it be anybody's room? Are there photographs, personal furniture, pictures on the walls, mementos -all*

When Brian started work on the west wing he noticed that the people who were immobile were continually slipping down from the standard high-seated straight backed chairs. He suggested that special chairs be purchased for those residents. Two reclining chairs were bought and tried. They proved to be a great success.

clearly showing a real individual's interests, tastes and background? Would the room say, for the occupant, 'This is my special place?'

-Seating arrangements. *Are chairs lined up in rows all round the room? Can some chairs be arranged so that people can be more easily in contact with each other? How are the needs of those who cannot walk catered for, so that they have enough contact? If space allows, is there a choice between sitting in a quieter area and in one where there is more action?*

-Space to move. *Is there room for those who want to walk around to do so in safety? Is enough effort being made to enable people to walk outdoors?*

All the practical matters that we have looked at are important, and need our attention. Being efficient is part of giving really good care. Beyond these things there's something else, which we all know about, but which is much harder to get hold of. What really makes a place homely or not is the people who are there, and the atmosphere they create. The best furniture, the smartest curtains, the most up-to-date apparatus - these things do not, in the end, make a house into a home. Even some places that are quite shabby have a cheerful and welcoming feel about them. The special magic is created by people and their attitudes. If they are relaxed, warm, kind-hearted and caring, that will count above all else. A home is a place where each individual is valued as a person.

CHAPTER 7

LOOKING AT
SOME PROBLEMS

Anyone of any age, whose mental powers are in decline is likely to have great difficulty in living a happy and carefree life. The world will seem a more frightening and threatening place. People will seem less understanding, more remote, and it will be harder to recognize who they are. So confused people may feel very insecure at times and need a great deal of reassurance and support; also, they may be easily discouraged by failure. Older people, in addition to these difficulties, may be having to endure some of the common illnesses or handicaps of their age group, so it is easy to see how the problems of living can get them down.

Bear these things in mind when a confused person is causing you problems by their behaviour. However inconvenient or annoying the behaviour may be for you, try to be understanding. How would any of us manage, if we had to live with the losses and handicaps that they are facing?

There is another point to consider. It isn't simply that 'they' are the problem, and 'we' are the solution. The truth is that 'we' are often part of the problem as well, because of our lack of imagination, sensitivity, gentleness, or attention. When a problem does occur, try to see it not as something caused by 'them', but as a problem that we all share.

So don't rush in to tackle difficulties, going for the quickest solution. Instead, try asking yourself the following five questions.

- Is it really a problem - How often does it occur?

- Why is it a problem?

- Who is it a problem for? Have we as caregivers made it into a problem by being unwilling to change, adapt, accept?

- Is the person with the 'problem behaviour' trying to tell us something?

- How can this problem be resolved in a way which most enhances the person's quality of life?

'Problems' can simply melt away when caregivers ask and answer those four questions. So let's take a look now at seven of the common problem areas.

WANDERING

Many carers sense that wandering is a kind of searching; the confused person is lost, in a way. They may be looking for familiar places, or for a loved one, or trying to find company or security. A person may be feeling lifeless, not having enough stimulation; they may simply be wanting to experience the fact that they are alive. Often wandering and restlessness increase towards the evening. Why should this be? Perhaps in the evening there is less to make an impact on the senses. The daylight may have gone; there may be fewer sounds of human activity, and perhaps there are not so many people around. So a confused person who gets a sense of security from the feeling of being in company may begin to feel anxious or un-nerved.

There's no point in trying to stop people from wandering. Sedative medication is far more likely to make those who wander more confused than to make the 'problem' of wandering go away. It's better to make it possible for them to wander in safety.

There are, however, ways to help a 'wanderer' to feel more secure. You could try wandering with them for a while. Do they take your hand or your arm? Reassure them by what you say; tell them that they are safe and that there's always going to be someone nearby; they are not going to be abandoned. Keep changes in furniture or layout to the minimum, and don't make them towards the end of the day. It may help someone with a tendency to wander at night if a light is left on in the bedroom.

But not all wandering is brought on because of confusion. There could be several other causes. Perhaps the person wants to go to the toilet. Perhaps they are in some kind of pain. Perhaps their clothing isn't clean and comfortable. Perhaps they are simply bored. Most obvious of all, wandering may occur because a person is needing exercise. You could try helping them to get some more exercise each day, and giving them a more varied range of things to do. It's good to go to bed feeling healthily tired.

If the person is liable to go outside on their own there are several things to think about. Depending on the individual circumstances it may be necessary to keep doors onto the street locked, and perhaps to have locks in an unfamiliar place, such as near the bottom of the door. Be sure that the confused person has some

Mrs Wright seemed to do a lot of wandering. The house where she and her daughter, Chris, lived was small. Problems arose when it was too rainy or cold to go outside. One day Chris had a brainwave. She asked the vicar if it would be alright for her mother to wander with her in the church, which was very close to where they lived. The vicar agreed. Both mother and daughter enjoyed these visits, and sometimes they had organ music as well. It was Mrs. Wright's request which first drew the vicar's attention to the problem of dementia in his parish.

form of identification. If they do wander off, don't panic. It's unlikely that they will come to harm. Contact the police, who will help you to find them. Think about how to prevent it happening again. Also it may be better to accept a small degree of risk than to hem a person in completely, as if they were in prison.

INCONTINENCE

Many (although not all) people who are severely confused become incontinent at some point. For some it may just be that they have more or less given up hope and self-respect; and it is well known that continence can return when a person is offered more security, and given really kind and respectful care. So if a person you are looking after has become incontinent, the first thing to ask is this: are there any needs that aren't being met, and that could be met? But this is not the whole story. Some incontinence really does seem to be the result of damage that is occurring in the brain.

Try to understand how humiliating it must be to have lost control of bladder and bowels, and perhaps not even to know when an accident is about to occur. The ability to control these functions was developed in early childhood. It is a very private matter; perhaps it touches feelings of modesty at their most sensitive point. After an accident has occurred a person may feel extremely ashamed and embarrassed; they may try to hide the effects, perhaps by putting soiled clothing in a drawer or a cupboard. Don't be critical. Don't be like a scolding schoolteacher if an accident has occurred. Doing this kind of thing will only make them feel worse. The best way is to be quite matter-of-fact about what has happened, and simply to get on with the job of cleaning up. If you are kind and accepting, it doesn't mean that you are encouraging them to do it again. Rather, you are sparing their feelings and helping them to have more self-respect. This is the most likely way to avoid accidents in the future. The worst problem you may have to deal with is if a person seems deliberately to smear their faeces over the floor or the furniture. Sometimes this may be understood as a desperate bid for attention by someone who has almost lost hope.

If a person you are looking after has become incontinent, it is always a good idea to consult a doctor. There may be an infection in the urinary system, or some other physical problem that can be treated quite simply.

The incontinence may be a side-effect of drug treatment. It is also possible that they simply can't find their way to the toilet, or that they can't undo their clothing in time. For some people it may be helpful to have a commode in an obvious place. Clothing can be made easier to take off by sewing on velcro fastenings instead of zips or buttons. Plastic sheeting can be put over a mattress, under the bottom sheet. Something similar can be done for chairs. Disposable pads are available, as well as special protective knickers or pants. If you do use them, remember that they are specially designed for adults, not for babies! Take care to ensure that pads are changed as necessary, and that the genital area is clean and dry.

You may be able to work out a toiletting routine. To do this, keep careful note over several days of exactly when the person you are caring for needs to go to the toilet, and see if there is a pattern. If there is

one, you can work with it, and so help prevent accidents from happening. In a residential home, remember that each person is an individual, and that each one has their own toiletting pattern.

AGGRESSION

Some people whose mental powers are failing - whatever their age - may at times become very angry or even violent. This can be surprising and frightening. And for a family carer who is giving a great deal of time, energy and dedication, it can be extremely hurtful and distressing. Usually aggression is the result of severe frustration and insecurity.

- A person wants to say something, and finds that no one understands.

- They are wanting to do something, and no one will help them to do it.

- There's an annoyance or pain that they can do nothing about.

- They are troubled by being so dependent on others.

- They are angry that the failure of memory and all that goes with it should have happened to them.

Mr Cuthbertson was having difficulties. His wife had bladder problems, and several times now he had had to mop up after an accident. He just happened to hear about incontinence pads at a meeting for carers, run by the Alzheimer's Disease Society. He got hold of some the very next day, and they made all the difference.

Zena was new to the home. One day she 'thumped' another resident causing great distress. One careworker looked after the 'victim', and took her from the scene. Another careworker spoke gently to Zena: 'You're very upset, Zena, aren't you? I know it's not easy for you being here'. She asked Zena if she'd come into the kitchen and help with the drying up. Zena went along willingly.

Look for possible reasons such as these.

Try to understand, then, the perfectly human need that may underlie the aggression. Often this is something to do with power and control. A person who becomes permanently confused has lost so much control over their own life. Aggression may be one of the few forms of power that they still have. They may sense that people around them have too much power. One thing they can do, feeling so humiliated, is to find someone who is weaker and use crude power over them. Sometimes aggression has to do with being cut off from others, or feeling less than a living person. Perhaps then the only way left to get real attention and consideration is to create a violent scene of some kind. So aggression may be a message that a person is in desperate need of human contact, and of a life that still has meaning.

The best way to deal with aggressive behaviour, in the long term, is to find the underlying need and meet it. This isn't easy; also, it may take time before someone who has taken on aggressive patterns of behaviour feels secure enough to relax and change. In the short term, emergency action may be needed. So here are some guidelines for dealing with someone who is being dangerously aggressive.

- Be very calm. It will be all the more frightening for a very disturbed person if you seem to be out of control as well. Try to convey tenderness and reassurance by the tone of your voice.

- Give the person space. Don't crowd them out, or try to take hold of them, or remove them from the scene, as this can be felt as very threatening. Some people may respond to bodily contact; but don't take the risk if they are extremely out of control or they don't know you well. In any case, explain any movements you make and keep these to a minimum.

- Direct other people away from the scene, particularly anyone who may be at risk. Ask that no one should interfere. You may need help from others, but they should keep at a distance, and be out of sight if possible.

- Suggest something that the person can do so as to take their attention away from whatever it was that provoked the aggression.

What we are really talking about here is only a kind of 'first aid', and it doesn't really solve any underlying problems. Simply, there are times when it is necessary to take the heat out of what could be a nasty situation. The underlying needs still must be met where possible. After the person has calmed down and done something else for a little while, try asking them about what made them so upset and how it could be prevented in the future. (Of course, they may not be able to remember clearly, so don't overdo this). You may be able to look at the problem with others involved in caring. And in any case, it's best if you have already agreed on how you are going to deal with aggressive behaviour if and when it does occur.

HIDING AND LOSING

Some people with 'dementia' seem to develop a knack for losing things. This can make them feel even more confused and ashamed. Also, it can be extremely tiresome for a family member to discover that the front door key, or the rent book, or the unpaid electricity bill, or a favourite piece of jewellery has mysteriously disappeared.

Much of this kind of behaviour can be understood as an attempt to 'make things safe'. Imagine the situation of an older person who knows that their memory is not holding up well. They become worried that they won't know where things are. So the obvious answer is to put these things in a really safe place. The problem then is that they forget where the safe place is, and what it was that they were making safe!

But there may be more to this hiding and losing pattern than simply a desire to make particular articles safe. Maybe a person who is undergoing a dementing illness has the sense that things are continually being taken away. And it's true, in a way, isn't it? The worst thing of all is that part of their own self is being taken away, and they don't know how they are going to be in the future. Everything is changing, and for almost all who are in this condition it must seem to be a change for the worse. They themselves may feel terribly unsafe. Hiding things can sometimes be seen, then, as a kind of effort to stop anything more from being taken away.

Ron needed his marriage certificate in order to make some legal arrangements. He put it out ready to take into town. Then a little later he found it had vanished. Bessie, his wife, said she knew nothing about it. Ron then realised that he was going to need to be very careful about where he put valued items. It was only after Bessie had died, when Ron was going through her belongings, that he eventually found the marriage certificate, inside an old family bible.

Try to recognize any signs of feeling unsafe that the person you are looking after may show, and note the times and situations when they seem to feel most unsafe. Do all that you can to help them to feel safe and secure. You can reassure them with words, but also with your actions .

■ **For Family Carers**

Think of some of those familiar, happy and comforting things that have been there in the past:

- *a favourite walk or drive*
- *a special cake*
- *a treasured item of clothing*
- *coffee from a mug that has done long service*
- *a piece of music that brings back beautiful memories*

Things like these can make such a difference when a person feels unsafe.

You will need to be extremely practical and down-to-earth, if life isn't going to be made difficult through things disappearing. Make sure that all vital documents, money, cheque books, keys and such like are kept in some place where you know they will not be found. Do this tactfully, so that you don't seem to be conspiring against the person in your care.

REPETITIVE LANGUAGE, SCREAMING AND OTHER NOISES

Sometimes a person whose mental powers are failing seems to get stuck, rather like a record with a faulty groove, and says the same thing over and over again.

To be with a person who does this can be extremely wearing, and it may seem as if there's just no way to help them to stop. Sometimes, too, a severely confused person may scream, or moan, or wail, without any obvious cause.

There are many possible reasons for behaviours of this kind. It's a bit too easy just to say that they are a result of brain damage. Those who give out these sounds are still persons who have feelings. So here are some possible reasons why they do it.

- It may be a way of saying 'I'm distressed', or 'I'm anxious' or 'I'm lonely '.
- It may be a form of protest, 'Please take my needs into account', when too much is going on, or too fast.

- It may be a way of saying 'Please notice me. I'm still here.' Attention of some kind, even if it is being told to shut up, may feel better than getting no attention at all.
- It may be a kind of self-stimulation - almost a way for a person to prove to themselves that they are still alive. This means, of course, that far too little stimulation is being provided by other people.

So as with aggressive behaviour, look for signs that suggest what the person is really needing. You may find clues in the words that are used. Ellen, in the example above, was feeling lost and very much 'not at home' after being placed in residential care. You'll find out a good deal just by observing carefully, and using a bit of imagination.

SEXUALLY INAPPROPRIATE BEHAVIOUR

Those whose mental powers are failing, at whatever age, still have sexual needs and desires. Sexual feelings don't go away just because memory and other mental functions are in decline. For some people the opposite is true: as some parts of the mind work less well than before, the barriers against acting on their sexual desires also come down.

The question here for carers is how to help those they are looking after to cope with their sexuality. If you are the husband or wife or partner of a severely confused person, this may be a very difficult and sensitive area, especially if your sexual needs do not seem to match each other. If you are a carer of some other kind, the problems are different, and won't touch you so deeply. Responding directly to sexual overtures isn't the best thing, for obvious reasons; but it won't help if we ignore or criticize a person who is being sexually explicit in some way. It's better to be constructive, and here is a suggestion about our approach. Sexuality is a very complex mixture. There's a need for closeness, a need for warm affection, a need to feel one's manhood or womanhood, a need to feel accepted, a need for bodily contact, a need to feel alive, as well as obvious sexual desire. As a carer you may be able to respond to some of the needs that are being expressed, although not responding to the last.

Sometimes a person may begin to fondle their genitals or to stimulate

A careworker named Susan was helping Paul to get dressed. He tried to pull her down onto the bed, and told her that he wanted her sexually. She said to him, firmly but very kindly, 'Paul, I don't want to do that. But we could have a dance together. Come on, let's get you dressed'. She danced round the room with him when he was dressed, and then they went down to breakfast arm in arm. Paul looked very happy. Not everyone could manage it as Susan did, but that was her way.

themselves sexually, in a room where others are present. Again, recognize the underlying need. Be kind and understanding, even while making sure that the behaviour doesn't continue in a public place. As with some other kinds of 'problem behaviour', this may simply be a person's way of trying to keep the feeling of being alive when stimulation from outside is missing.

Sometimes we may think we are seeing sexual behaviour, and we get the message wrong.

As caregivers we need to accept sexuality as perfectly natural: our own, as well as that of those we care for. Sexuality is part of what makes us human, and it is bound up with almost every other aspect of our humanity. We all are sexual beings. Part of our skill in living is being wise and understanding about our own and others' sexual needs.

DELUSIONS HALLUCINATIONS, ACCUSATIONS

A delusion means believing something that's not true, such as that children who are adults are still young, or that a parent long dead is still alive. A hallucination means seeing, hearing or feeling something that isn't really there, such as getting the impression that the curtains are going up in flames. Delusions and hallucinations have many possible causes other than 'dementia.' Among these are infections, high levels of drugs, dehydration and the after-effects of long periods of heavy drinking. A doctor can help in checking on what may be the cause.

The delusions and hallucinations that are really part of a dementing illness need understanding rather than treatment. Often we will find that they have a meaning, if we keep an open mind. So if a person in your care has them, there's no point in saying that these experiences are not real or true; but also, you don't need to pretend that you yourself are believing or seeing exactly the same. Listen carefully, and catch a sense of the feelings that are being conveyed as well. They may be trying to tell you something about their hopes or fears, their joys or pains, in their own special language.

So, respect the 'reality' of the person you are caring for, even though it is different from yours. If you are struggling hard to bring them to your sense of reality, ask yourself why you are doing it. Are you simply trying to relieve your own sense of discomfort? Are you trying to uphold your authority? If what you are doing really does have a point - if it really does add to their well-being - that's fine. But if not, relax and let things be. In any case, always accept and respect each person just as they are.

People who are confused sometimes make wild accusations. They might say that they have been attacked, perhaps, or that you have taken something from them, or that burglars are breaking in and you're not stopping them. Often accusations and suspicions such as these have a clear meaning, when you take into account their failing memory and deep sense of personal insecurity.

PERSONS, NOT PROBLEMS

One last thing about these so-called 'problem behaviours.' Carers often try to shape or mould a severely confused person's behaviour so that the problems don't occur so often. As a general idea, that's fine. But don't focus on the problem behaviour. Above all, don't criticize or condemn it; if you do this, you may in fact be encouraging the behaviour, although you aren't aware of the fact. Focus on the person, not the problem, and seek out how to meet needs in ways that do not involve so much difficulty. There's no magical answer, no set of special 'tricks of the trade.' Perhaps some of the problems are there to stay. But if your whole approach is person-centered, not problem-centered, the one you are caring for will be very much happier; and so will you.

Edna talks to her husband as if he were still there, although he has been dead for ten years. Perhaps she is longing for the companionship and security she had with him when he was alive.

Margaret sometimes looks out into the garden and sees faces in the trees, angry and menacing. When she does this her husband, Dick, doesn't try to 'put her straight'. He realizes that she's frightened, and that the faces are real enough to her. So he holds her hand or hugs her gently, and reminds her that she's safe indoors with him.

CHAPTER 8

THE QUESTION
OF DRUGS

When someone we care for isn't well, and we seem unable to help them, we generally turn to the doctor. Sometimes just the right drug is available, and it quickly brings about good effects. In the case of a genuine dementing illness, linked to one or both of the types of brain damage mentioned on page 10, no drug has yet been found that definitely helps. There are some drugs on trial that may slow down the process of cell loss in the brain, and some that may help the brain cells to work more efficiently. But it will be a long time yet before a miracle drug appears. Possibly this will never happen. At present most of the real help is going to come from human beings, giving truly personal care.

Actually, as many doctors are now realising, drugs are sometimes part of the problem. It is quite often found that older people are taking too many drugs, or in the wrong doses; some have simply carried on for years getting a renewed prescription, adding other drugs from time to time. Their bodies - and their brains - may be reacting badly to the drugs. Sleeping tablets, for instance, which are effective at first, may build up in the body over time and cause confusion. Some older people have taken them for years. So doctors who specialise in work with older people sometimes try for a while to get new patients off all drugs that are not absolutely essential. Then they see how the patients really are, and start treatment again. Since drugs may take some time to pass out of an older person's body, this whole process takes several weeks, or even months. Similarly, when older people show signs of confusion, some doctors try to reduce all drugs to the minimum, in case it is these that are having bad effects. Most professionals involved in care for confused people now aim to use as little as possible of drugs that affect the brain.

Tranquillizers are sometimes used to reduce the agitation, aggression, or other 'problem behaviours' such as those we have looked at. Unfortunately it is all too easy at present to give careworkers a let-out by prescribing this kind of medication. It does, in a way, make an individual more 'manageable'; but the trouble is, it makes them less of a person. If a person's behaviour becomes too difficult to manage, whether at home or in a care scheme, something has to be done. The care practice may be inadequate, and so additional supervision may be needed. In some cases a different care scheme might be tried, but the reasons for and against would need to be weighed up carefully. Tranquillizers are a 'last resort'.

Anti-depressant drugs are a different matter. There seems to be more ground for using them in certain cases. Many people who are confused are also depressed. Often this is understandable when we consider the losses and life changes they have had to undergo. Sometimes the depression is so deep and lasting that drug treatment may be the best answer, in the short term at any rate. It is often found that as the depression lifts, so also does some of the confusion. However, don't look on anti-depressants as the key to all problems of lowered mood. A great deal can be done to help depression simply through human contact and understanding. What's more, this has absolutely no harmful side-effects!

If drugs that modify mood or behaviour are used, their effect should be regularly and carefully checked. It is important to know whether they really are doing what they were intended for. This is not just the responsibility of doctors, who are only around for a very short time. As a carer it is also your responsibility, as you know far more about what's happening on a day to day basis. It is best that you know something about what medication is being used, and what it is supposed to do. In particular, get information about possible side-effects, and look out for these. You don't need to be medically trained in order to have some impression of the effect of a drug. If you keep track of both positive and negative effects, this will be of great help to those who actually take the decisions about giving drugs. They may be the experts on the medication, but you are the expert on the person in your care.

When Matthew was in hospital he was violent and genuinely 'demented'. He was disliked and feared. He was on a heavy dose of haloperidol and two major tranquillizers. Also he was being given a drug called androcur, which lowers the male sex drive. Then he was taken into residential care, where the policy was to reduce drugs to the minimum. With a doctor's guidance Matthew was taken off all four drugs, over six months. He had severe withdrawal symptoms, and became very agitated at times; also he had terrifying hallucinations. The care staff supported him through all of this. When he was finally off the drugs, he settled into the life of the home. He became an alert, vigorous but confused old man, with great need for reassurance. The staff became very fond of him.

55

PLANNING

PERSONAL CARE

▲ For Careworkers

If care is to be truly personal, we will need to have detailed knowledge about each person for whom we are responsible, and to be clear about how we intend to provide care for them. We looked at this question in a general way in chapter 2 (page 13). In any group care setting, it is especially important to do this more systematically, because there it can be so easy to lose the sense that each person is special.

If you work in a formal care setting you may already be involved in recording and discussing written assessments and care plans. Reading this section over may give you ideas on how to improve your current approach. If you give care in a small or very informal scheme, the idea of individual assessment and planning may be new to you or the people you work with. If that is the case, see if you and your co-workers can establish a simple but regular method to begin with. The value will soon become clear to all. It isn't merely added and unnecessary paperwork and meeting time. It is a vital opportunity to reflect on the care that

you are providing and the reasons why it is given. Also you may be able to see how care can be improved.

Whether your planning is undertaken formally or quite informally, it is important for the whole care team to be involved: direct carers, specialists, managers, family members, and of course the person who is receiving care - where this is possible. Depending on the circumstances, support staff such as cleaners and kitchen helpers may also have something to contribute to this process. However it is done, it is important that records are kept, and that there is some way for information to be shared with every member of the team.

The essential elements of this whole process are assessment, care plans, monitoring and reassessment. Let's look at each in more detail.

The assessment of an individual needs to take into account the whole person. It should identify their strengths and abilities, every bit as much as pointing out relevant areas of weakness or disability. As assessments are often used to provide a written 'snapshot' of the person, wording is extremely important. Be accurate, but use positive rather than negative language wherever possible. Consider, for example, the brief admission assessments on pages 60 and 61.

Notice how differently one might feel about Miss Smith, depending on whether the first or second assessment was read.

Care plans are used by carers to identify need areas, set up workable goals and offer guidelines on how to achieve them. As with assessments, it is important that they are positive in tone and person-centred. It is all too human to attend to only the most obvious problems, the ones which cause us the most difficulty. However, needs should be understood as far as possible from the point of view of those we care for. Also, when thinking about needs, avoid focusing just on problems. Personal strengths, interests and preferences are also 'need areas'; each individual needs positive help, in all kinds of ways. Assessments and life histories can help when care plans are being drawn up.

Once needs have been identified, try to translate them into some definite plan of action. It will help to state an objective or goal for each need; putting it into clear and direct words. Make the goals realistic. For example, there would be no sense in stating 'improve memory' as a goal when we know this is not likely to be achieved. However, 'be able to locate bedroom and toilet' may be a workable target. Sometimes it may help to make a division between long and short term objectives. Once these have been agreed upon, a little creative brainstorming will often be the best way to come up with a list of ways to attain them. Here you will need to be very specific: state exactly what needs to be done, when and by whom. Usually, phrases like 'ongoing support by staff' contribute little to your care planning. Such generalities can't be pinned down.

Compare the following extracts from care plans for Miss Smith:

Care plans at St. Luke's Nursing home had always been prepared by the senior nurses. They focused entirely on physical and memory problems. Then a new policy was tried. Direct careworkers, activities staff and family carers all shared in the drawing up of the care plans. In a very short time, people began to notice that the atmosphere of the home seemed more lively and the residents began to stand out as real individuals.

Assessment 1

Miss Lena Smith is a quiet, generally good humoured lady. Except for arthritis, she is in excellent health, and seems to enjoy walking about the building. Though confused, she recognizes people with whom she is familiar, and has good long-term memory. In keeping with her former patterns of coping, she is slowly but steadily adjusting to her new environment, and has developed a good relationship with her roommate. Miss Smith currently prefers one-to-one, and other quiet social activities.

From Care Plan 1

Need: New to Glendale, states she doesn't feel she belongs here.

Goal: To develop a few meaningful relationships with other residents.

Plan: As alternative to weekly singalong, suggest an afternoon walk outside with her room-mate and one other resident who Miss Smith might enjoy as a companion. Staff to accompany for first month.

Goal: Make surroundings more familiar.

Plan: 1. By next week, staff leader will invite Miss Smith and her daughter for a meeting to discuss how to personalize bedroom.

2. Miss Smith responds better to pictures than words - by end of week, primary careworker will invite her to put her photo on bedroom door.

3. Ask her brother, on his next visit, whether there are any pictures from Miss Smith's former home.

Assessment 2

Lena Smith is a confused wanderer who lacks orientation to time and place and has very poor short-term memory. She complains frequently about her arthritis. She has not yet adjusted to her new environment, but has always had problems adjusting to change so this is not surprising. She isn't good with groups of people, and tends to scream and cry during large group activities, which disrupts and upsets the other residents.

From Care Plan 2

Problem: *New to Home, states she doesn't belong here.*

Plan: *Remind her that this is her new home now and give ongoing support and encouragement. Label door with her name.*

Problem: *Disruptive during group activities.*

Plan: *Seat in far back of room area during singalong, reinforce non-disruptive behaviour.*

Problem: *Bedroom looks uninviting: family did not bring in any belongings for bedroom.*

Plan: *Put up some colourful wall pictures to make it look cheery.*

Notice how the first extract uses goals and personal information about Miss Smith to make the plan more person-centered than problem-centered. Also because the first plan indicates dates and responsible staff, it is more likely to be carried out.

Monitoring *is a way of keeping track of how the person you care for is doing, and specifically, how they are responding to the care you are providing. With all we have to do, it is easy to go from planning discussion to planning discussion without giving much thought to how things are going for each individual in the meanwhile. The problem with this, though, is that our memories have their limits as well, and sometimes ideas and insights become lost in time. Regular monitoring prevents this from happening. It may be sufficient simply to jot down relevant notes in a log book on a daily or other regular basis, or perhaps short progress meetings where notes are taken will be preferred. One further idea about monitoring is given on pages 75-76.*

Reassessment *is the last element in the care planning cycle; it doesn't complete the picture because assessment and planning will need to go on continually, as the person in our care changes. Here we assess any progress that has been made, note any changes needed to our approaches and bring up any new need areas. We will inevitably find that some of what we tried just didn't work. This does not mean failure, because we will undoubtedly have learned something in the process, about the individual we are caring for or about the nature of caregiving itself.*

Care planning and assessment, then, enable us to give really good individual care despite having a heavy workload. But there is something more. Caregiving in this way can be more rewarding for us as professionals. It makes better use of our wealth of experience and lets us be more creative and resourceful. It also aids communication and understanding between carers and other members of the team. And, perhaps most rewarding of all, by keeping track of things we will be able to see the difference we are making in the lives of those we are looking after.

THE MOVE INTO

RESIDENTIAL

CARE

■ For Family Carers

The majority of people, including those whose mental powers are failing, will live out their years in their own home, or in the home of a close relative. However, the time may come for some when other alternatives will have to be considered. Anyone who is involved in a decision to place someone close to them into residential care is likely to find it very difficult. For many, it may be the most painful decision they will ever have to face.

Those caring for a frail older person usually base the decision clearly on questions of physical need. Perhaps they require lifting, or specialized nursing care, which simply can't be provided within the home by an unqualified carer. However, the decision to place a generally healthy but mentally confused person into residential care may not be as straightforward. The main reasons for such a move may have more to do with the needs of the carer. Constant sleep disruptions, challenging problem behaviours, or the demands of keeping a 24-hour watchful eye may be too much. These burdens may be causing great emotional and even physical distress to the carer, or perhaps the carer's family.

More and more efforts are being made to assist family carers so that they can continue to provide care at home. But services may be patchy, or insufficient for what is required. Sometimes, meeting all the needs of the confused person means seriously neglecting the carer's own needs. If you are in such a situation, be honest with yourself and the person you care for. You may have feelings of guilt which will only be made worse if you deny that your needs are being considered in the decision as well.

CHOOSING A RESIDENTIAL HOME

If residential care may be needed soon, it is wise to plan ahead. The issue is usually so difficult and painful that families tend to put off looking into it until things become completely unbearable. This isn't a good idea because the time needed to explore options may be more limited then. As with all of the services offered to confused persons and their carers, the best strategy is to learn all you can about what is available before it is needed, and then to only use the service at the point when it really makes sense to do so.

If you are not familiar with residential care schemes, you may be surprised to discover how much variety there is. There are different levels of care and different systems for care. Even homes which fall into the same category may be very different from one another when you get inside .

Local Authority Old People's Homes were mainly intended to care for mentally alert but frail elderly persons, although it is estimated that nowadays nearly half of the residents in such homes have some degree of confusion. These homes generally do not have staff trained in dealing with confusion, although 'specialist' homes or 'dementia care wings' of larger homes do exist in certain areas, and staff training programmes are being introduced more and more. Costs are determined by a test of the person's income and assets, and may vary from one Authority to another. Application is made by a social worker. Unfortunately, more often than not a long wait is involved, although immediate admission can sometimes be arranged if it is a matter of urgency.

The number of *Private Residential Homes* has quickly grown over the last decade. The quality varies widely; probably both the best and worst care are to be found in the private sector. Of course, there is a profit motive to be considered, although many private homes are strongly committed to good caring; in any case, they have to be concerned with quality in order to be competitive. The cost of care is usually subsidized by DSS, subject to a means test. Many homes charge additional fees, and some are willing to negotiate the amount. Application is made direct to the home. Waiting lists are sometimes shorter than Local Authority homes, but this varies. If a home has a very short list, try to discover why.

Nursing Homes are run by Local Authority, the private sector, or voluntary organisations. These have fully qualified nursing staff on duty day and night and are intended for persons who require skilled nursing care. Therefore, generally only confused persons who also have physical and medical care needs are appropriate for this level. The costs of nursing homes are met in a very similar way to that for residential homes, but the basic sum allocated by DSS is much higher.

Many areas have hospitals with dementia care wings. Long term beds are usually scarce; typically care for confused people in hospital is given

Mrs Mack was looking for a residential home for her mother. When she visited Dale View, which specialized in dementia care, she could not come to terms with what she saw. She found a place for her mother at Castle Ridge, which was beautifully furnished and decorated, but where there was no real understanding for confused people. After four months Mrs Mack was asked to take her mother away because of her behaviour problems. Mrs Mack now arranged for her mother to go to Dale View . She soon settled in, and got on well with both residents and staff.

for short periods - either for assessment and treatment, or a few weeks of respite. The cost is covered by the NHS, although after one year the person's State Pension and Social Security payments and allowances may be reduced or stopped. Application is made by a visiting nurse.

PLAN A VISIT

When thinking about residential care, do make visits. It is the only way you can be sure that a home is the right one for the person you care for.

There will be many things to consider in your choice. When visiting, it may help to bring along a checklist such as the one shown below. The Alzheimer's Disease Society also puts out a helpful booklet called What to Look for in Residential Care. Ask lots of questions and take notes while you are there. The staff of any good home will encourage you to do so and will take time to discuss all of your concerns. Here are some suggestions about questions to ask and what to look for when you visit. You might also like to refer back to Chapter 7, (page 41).

-Is it near enough for you and others to visit as often as you would like?

-Is the general appearance bright, pleasant and homely? Being especially beautiful or modern isn't particularly important, but avoid places that seem more like a clinic or museum. Is space used creatively, or are seats simply lined up along the walls? Is there room to move around, particularly if someone likes to walk about frequently? Is there a safe outside area, ideally with inviting gardens and places to sit?

-Are the bedrooms sterile or personal? Are photos and other mementos encouraged? Is personal furniture allowed? Does each room contain a toilet and sink? Single rooms are generally better than shared rooms, but are not always available.

-Do residents appear alert and comfortable? Do you see smiles, laughter and friendly interaction? Avoid places where the residents simply sit motionless, looking vacant and uninterested; also places where there is chaotic commotion and an air of distress and anxiety. The common room

should be relatively quiet except for areas where activity and socializing are taking place.

-What is the percentage of confused residents? Are there other residents who seem similar to your relative in their level of confusion? There is much disagreement over which is preferable: a specialist home or one which has both confused and non-confused residents. Some feel that segregation labels people and that those who are confused can benefit from being with those who are not. However, it is often the case that residents whose mental powers are intact get impatient with those where powers are failing. Despite good arguments on both sides, there simply isn't one 'right' approach. Let your own judgement guide you as to what seems to be best for the person you care for.

-Do the residents look well-groomed? Has attention been given to their clothing and hair? Is there a visiting hairdresser?

-To what extent are residents enabled to make choices? Are there menu options? Is there a kitchenette area for residents' use so that they can make a cup of tea or get a drink of water themselves? Are residents asked about their preferences, or are things simply done for or to them?

-Is there a varied activities programme? Are there both regular activities and special events, like parties, barbecues or entertainment evenings? Sometimes it is implied that activities occur more regularly than they really do. To get a more realistic idea, ask about what activities took place that particular week, and exactly when was the last special occasion.

-To what extent do residents make contact with the community? Are there pubs, parks, shops and so on close by, and how often do residents frequent them? Are there any community members who come into the home to visit, entertain, or provide a service?

Do members of the clergy visit, or can this be arranged if desired? Is there a transport vehicle available to take residents on outings?

-What is the staffing level? It may be difficult to determine whether this is adequate, but do enquire. Although there isn't a standard formula, there should be sufficient day and night time staff so that *personal care can be given, and substitutes should be called in whenever regular staff are absent.*

-Is there an ongoing programme for staff training? Even in mixed care homes, staff should receive training in caring for confused people.

-How flexible or rigid is the daily routine? Does everyone get up and go to bed at a certain time? Is there choice around bathing? How are refusals handled? Ask for a description of a typical day.

GETTING SETTLED

Becoming adjusted to a new place takes plenty of time: time for things to become familiar, time to get to know people well, time to build up a sense of belonging. Like anyone else, a person with a dementing illness will probably feel anxious and lost at first in their new surroundings. However, it may be even more difficult because they may lack the mental skills which we generally rely on to cope with new situations. Therefore, a slow adjustment is to be expected, but at a human level we can aim to make the difficulties much less.

The first steps can be taken before your relative even makes the move,

by preparing them for what is about to happen. No matter how much you feel he or she may or may not understand, try to discuss the move with them and be honest. Listen and respond to their concerns, and offer reassurance and support. Involve them in whatever way possible; help them to pack their own suitcase, for example, and let them choose which belongings, pieces of furniture, and so on they wish to take. The move will be easier if they had previously been attending the home through day or respite care. Where this has not been possible, arrange for them to visit in advance.

Once your relative has moved in, both of you will need support in adjusting. Both of you will be having to deal with the loss and change. It is a good idea to visit frequently at first if at all possible. This will help them to understand that you haven't abandoned them. It may help you to realise this too, if you are feeling guilty and unsure. If you are readily available to answer any questions staff may raise, this will enable them to offer more personal care right away. As a result you will feel better too. In the course of time your visits may become less frequent, but try to keep them regular.

Many people feel uncomfortable visiting residential homes or hospitals. The heart of these feelings may be that we don't like to come face-to-face with a difficult fact of life - our own independence is fragile. We can sometimes overcome our anxiety by developing relationships within the home with staff, other residents, and other visiting families. By relating to the residents as individuals, we can often see past the hardships that they're having to deal with as they become more dependent on others.

Sometimes recognition fades, and this can be painful to accept. You may feel there is no point in visiting any more. But even if the person doesn't seem to recognize you or forgets your name, the chances are that they still have a sense that you are someone special to them. Your visits may touch something deep within them, even if they can't communicate it to you.

Try to stay actively involved in their care. The staff of most good homes will encourage and welcome you to do so, but you may need to be a bit assertive if they don't. Ask questions. Make suggestions. Discuss any and all of your concerns. Achieving the most personal care possible requires a team approach amongst all of the carers, including yourself.

Yours may have been a very difficult relationship in recent years, or perhaps always. However, you may find that without the responsibility of daily care an improved relationship becomes possible.

And finally, if the person you were looking after had been living with you previously, there may be feelings of grief to be worked through. Chapter 14 (page 89) takes a closer look at this.

George and May had had a long marriage, 57 years in all. There had been good times and bad times, but something sweet and romantic remained. When May became very forgetful George looked after her. He got very tired and cross, and then his back let him down. A place was found for May in residential care. George visited regularly. May never called him by his name, and she did not seem to be sure who he was. But they would sit together quietly for an hour or so, hand in hand, perhaps like they did when they were in their twenties. Both of them seemed to have found a kind of peace.

THE BEST WE
CAN HOPE FOR

When we are close to someone whose mental powers are failing, there is likely to be a feeling of change all around. Nothing is quite as it used to be, and the person we once knew so well seems to be slipping from our grasp. It may well seem like change for the worse; as we find that there is less and less that we can do together, while the burdens tend to increase. As a family carer your own needs may be pressing, and perhaps you may be wondering what the future will hold. And when you think about the one you are caring for, what is the best that you might hope for?

For that person, living with constant and probably growing confusion, life must be extremely difficult. We have explored the reasons why at many points in this book. There may even come a time when they don't recognize those whom they have known for years; they might even not recognize you yourself, although feeling that they know you well. All this, and the other problems, might seem to be a tragedy, and the ending of a life in ruins. But it doesn't have to be so, if the person you are caring for can be sufficiently secure, sufficiently free from anxiety, sufficiently loved and valued. The losses would still be hard to accept, but they wouldn't matter quite so much. We, as carers, will not be able to take away all suffering from them, but we may be able to keep it within bounds. In fact, of course, no human life is free from suffering; much as we might wish to, we cannot protect from pain even those whom we love dearly. We will not be able to share so much of their private 'reality,' as it moves further and further away from our own; but we may be able to give that reality a good deal of contentment and peace. Some people, in their confusion, actually become more playful and carefree. Some who have had a strong personal faith may still feel, at a very deep level, the love of God.

The best, then, that we can hope for is that the person in our care will be able to 'relax into' and accept the state of confusion, feeling secure and supported, and having the underlying sense that his or her needs will be met. When the time comes to die, they may be able to let go easily, and die in peace.

SIGNS OF SUCCESS

So, whether we are family carers or professionals of some kind, we will want to know whether or not our work is succeeding. The person we are looking after may not tell us in so many words, and they may seem to take all our efforts for granted. But there are certain marks or signs which clearly show that someone with failing mental powers is 'doing well' as a person. These signs, or some of them at least, can be present however weak memory or other parts of the mind may be.

Here are twelve such 'marks of well-being', with an example of each:

-Being able to assert one's own will or desires

May has had both courses of her evening meal, and has gone to sit down in an armchair. A carer, not realizing she had had both courses, brings the dessert to her, and tries to feed her. May says she doesn't want the food: the carer tries to coax her. May continues to refuse. The carer desists. Later the truth is discovered.

-Being able to express a range of emotions, of both happiness and distress.

Della is at home. Suddenly she looks exceedingly troubled. Her carer sits next to her and puts an arm around her. Della collapses into uncontrollable grief and sobbing. The carer continues to hold her, quietly and patiently. After a quarter of an hour or so Della begins to recover her composure, and soon afterwards is eager to go outside for a stroll in the sunshine.

-Initiating contact with others

David has a small dog, a soft toy, which he evidently treasures. He goes over to a woman sitting down, with her zimmer frame in front of her. He perches the dog on the zimmer frame, and tries to use it to attract her attention.

-Being affectionate

Helen lives in a large residential home. She swiftly walks back and forth between wings. Whenever someone says 'hello' to her, she stops for a moment to give them a friendly kiss on the cheek, and then continues on her way.

-Being sensitive to the needs and feelings of others

Cathy, a home care assistant, is feeling low in spirits, for reasons that have nothing to do with her work situation. When she arrives Agnes comes close to her, looks her in the face, and says, 'You're not so good today, dear, are you?' Cathy squeezes her hand, and says 'I'm feeling a bit sad, Agnes, but I'm here.' Agnes smiles and squeezes Cathy's hand. Somehow Agnes seems to understand.

-Having self-respect

Harriet has suddenly defaecated on the floor of the sitting room at home while her carer was using the vacuum cleaner upstairs. She begins to wipe up the mess with her cardigan.

-Accepting other confused people

Rose is a vigorous wanderer; she moves fast around the residential home. She catches hold of the hand of Kate, who is also wandering, but much more slowly. Kate accepts the hand and allows herself to be 'walked around' for a while, even though the pace is so different from her own.

-Enjoying humour

At a day care centre, Arthur enquires of Norman, 'Did you kiss your wife this morning?' Norman thinks for a moment, 'I can't remember.' Then he adds, with a twinkle in his eye, 'But if I didn't she'll play the devil with me when I get home!'

-Self-expression, being creative

There has been a session of singing, with accompaniment from the piano. Now the pianist is tired. Bridie stands up and sings an old Irish song, in a trembling voice but almost perfectly in tune, and with great depth of feeling. At the end, tears are running down her cheeks.

-Showing pleasure

Mrs Aston lives at home with her daughter, and attends a day care centre. She almost always smiles happily when she sees the minibus drive up in the mornings, and she is usually in a very cheery mood when she comes home, even though she can't say where she has been or what she has done.

-Being able to relax

Danielle has a habit of lying on the floor, curled up and tense. Her arms and legs shake and her face is in a grimace. Her son arrives; he gently takes her hands and guides her towards a sofa. He invites her to sit with him. In a few moments she has settled down, and cuddles close to him. Her body relaxes and her face becomes calm.

-Helpfulness

Joanne, a new volunteer, enters the sitting room. She sees a group of ladies chatting around the fire. A stern-looking man called Mr Parker is wandering alone, up and down; he seems not to be showing interest in anyone. Joanne joins the ladies. As there are no seats nearby, she sits on the floor. Soon afterwards, Mr

Parker comes by with a cushion he has taken from a chair and hands it to her without saying a word.

Notice here that well-being doesn't depend on a person's memory, or on abilities such as being able to follow a cooking recipe. The signs are telling us, rather, about a person's feelings, about their inner security and freedom from fear, about whether they are able to be content. Each sign shows that they've got a little bit extra - that they are not shut in themselves in suffering or despair. They are signs of hope; not hope that things will improve, but a sense that beyond the confusion the person is safe and well.

A WAY OF KEEPING CHECK

Now here's a method for following, week by week, how someone in your care is doing; in a way it's also a guide to whether you are having success in helping them to continue to be a person. You could draw up a chart like the one shown below, and keep it with any other records you are making. In this way you can build up a history of how the person in your care has been getting on. Think about the first sign: being able to assert one's own will or desire. Ask yourself whether, during the last week, the person in your care has shown this sign often, or sometimes, or never. If the answer is often, score 2; if sometimes, score 1; and if never, score 0. Do the same for each of the other signs, and add up the scores to get a total. If a person had shown all the signs frequently the score would be 2 x 12 = 24. If, on the other hand, a person had shown none of the signs during the last two weeks, the score would be 0. It's only a very rough-and-ready guide, and you've got to judge with each sign whether to give 2, 1 or 0. When a person is getting 12 or more, it suggests that care is going pretty well. When a person is getting very low scores, it suggests that the present situation is not a good one; changes are required, and more person-to-person care is needed. If you're a family member giving most of the care, it may mean that you are needing more support. Perhaps you could get advice from someone at your local branch of the Alzheimer's Disease Society. Possibly the task is now too much for you to take on at home by yourself.

Keeping a record of this kind will set you up to notice things more carefully. Also you'll become more aware that there can be plenty of good life for a person whose mental powers are failing.

LOOKING TOWARDS THE END

As a family carer, you may find that it is possible to keep the person whom you are looking after at home right until the point of their death. Extra help may be needed, and the amount of help will probably increase. It may be that your relative will not be able to stay at home, but needs full-time residential care. In either case, you can reasonably hope that some of the marks of well-being will be clearly shown right the way through .

Signs of Well-Being	2/2/91	9/2/91	16/2/91	23/2/91	2/3/91
1. Assertiveness	0	0	0	0	0
2. Range of Emotions	1	1	1	1	1
3. Initiating Contact	1	1	1	1	1
4. Affection	2	1	2	2	1
5. Sensitivity	0	1	1	1	1
6. Self Respect	0	0	0	0	0
7. Acceptance	2	2	1	1	2
8. Humour	1	0	2	2	1
9. Creative Expression	2	2	2	2	2
10. Pleasure	1	2	2	2	2
11. Relaxation	0	0	1	2	1
12. Helpfulness	0	1	1	1	1
Total	10	11	14	15	13

A MATTER OF
RIGHTS

There's a lot of talk these days about people's rights. The idea of a 'right' is a simple one. It means what individuals are entitled to, simply because they are human. In certain countries, such as Britain, very few rights are actually backed up by the law. In other countries, such as the USA, a whole range of citizens' rights have legal backing.

Thinking about rights helps to ensure that people will be treated respectfully by others, and especially that they will not be forced to do things against their will. So here's a list of rights for those whose mental powers are failing. It's based in part on suggestions that have been made about the rights of older people in residential care. One day, perhaps, a list such as this may become law in all countries.

-To be treated as individuals, and to have the opportunity to assert their own tastes and preferences.

-To associate with anyone they choose; to be enabled to maintain existing friendships and relationships.

-To be given privacy for themselves, their belongings and their affairs.

-To be involved as far as possible in the planning of their own care, and for their main family carer(s) to be involved as well.

-To be made aware of and to have access to the facilities and services of the community.

-To have a choice of suitable leisure activities, and the chance to engage in these on a regular basis.

-To receive a high standard of medical and physical care.

-To have their cultural, religious and sexual needs respected.

-To be able to make complaints and receive a proper response; also for complaints to be made on their behalf.

-To have a place to live which is safe and secure, and which is as homely as possible.

-To receive forms of support and care that do not exploit the goodwill of relatives and friends.

-To take reasonable risks which will add to their quality of life.

-To be as independent as possible.

-To do things at their own pace.

-Not to be restrained physically, or through the use of drugs, in the course of care.

-To be informed of these rights, and for their family to be informed as well.

Some of these 'rights' are easy to uphold. Probably you have been doing so most of the time, without noticing it. For most carers it seems natural to try to treat a person like this. You have always been mindful of their modesty when helping them to have a bath. You have always kept an eye on their medical and physical needs. But some of the other rights aren't so clear and easy to respect. The biggest difficulties come when someone isn't able to make reasonable decisions any more, and when the idea that they have rights can't be understood. It's then that we tend to feel we should protect them; we want to step in and take decisions for them. Sometimes there is no alternative. Perhaps the hardest decision of all is that a person should be taken into residential care, even though they have said that they don't want to go. The point here is that other people, including family members, have rights too.

However, people whose mental powers are beginning to fail are sometimes treated by others as if they can't make any decisions at all. If so, there has been a serious failure to respect their rights.

So we should consider carefully whether a person can or cannot make their own decisions. We need to keep track of this as time goes on and their abilities change. The question of risks is especially difficult when a person is in residential care. Those who run a home don't want to be accused of neglect, and may over-protect people, even when they see it is not really desirable.

One solution to this problem is for the manager to discuss risk-taking fully with relatives, and if possible with the person who is being taken into the home. The agreement they reach can be included in the contract. If matters are sorted out at the start, there will be fewer problems later on. And in general, if we find that we are tempted to over-protect a person, we could ask ourselves a question. Is this in their best interests, or is it more for our own convenience and peace of mind?

STANDING UP FOR RIGHTS

What should you do if you see that someone's rights are not being properly respected? If you are a really good carer yourself, it may be that your example will show a better way, and this will be sufficient. But there are times when more than this is required. Perhaps you know that a person's rights are being seriously

Iris had fallen several times and after one fall had been taken into hospital. She then went into a residential home. Now she was kept from walking around unless a care assistant was there to help her - lest she should fall and break her hip. As things worked out, there were some days when the only times she walked were when she went to the toilet, with the aid of a carer. Fairly soon she began to lose her ability to walk, and then after two months she was unable to walk independently at all. Iris was now far worse off - and all because her right to take a reasonable risk had not been respected.

violated, and it's obvious that harm is being done. It may then be necessary to take immediate action. This won't be easy, but it can be done in a helpful and positive way. You yourself could speak to the person responsible, directly and clearly challenging what they are doing. If so, don't sound like a know-all, or make a personal attack. Be a listener, and hear their point of view. In some instances it might be necessary to speak with a supervisor or manager. If so, be tactful - not accusing. Wherever a service is provided there may be a ready-made procedure for dealing with complaints. Would it be possible to use it? Bear in mind that when abuses do occur it's very rare indeed for these to involve deliberate cruelty or ill-will; it's much more likely that they arise from ignorance, fear, or overwork. Assigning blame isn't the important thing; the key is to correct the situation and find ways to ensure that it doesn't happen again.

RIGHTS AND PERSONS

The discussion of rights boils down to one simple but very important point. If we respect an individual's rights we are treating them as a person. If we disregard their rights, or suggest that they don't have any, we are treating them as a thing or an object. That's why considering rights is one of the key factors in person-to-person care.

WHAT ABOUT
OURSELVES ?

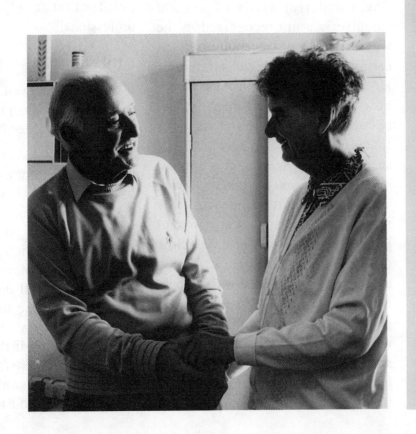

Caring for a person in need, whether it is done as a paid job, voluntarily, or because of family ties, is the most human kind of work. It can be done with complete sincerity. It involves us at each level of our being: body, mind and spirit. If we enter into it fully, it can bring great rewards. If we are close to the one we are looking after, caring may bring great pain and sorrow, but in and amongst that there can also be great joy.

The wonderful skills of a good caregiver are not recognized in the way that they deserve. The task of caring requires a special mixture of kindness, insight and practical know-how such as is found in very few occupations. Compare it, for instance, with the work of an accountant, an engineer, or a hospital manager. So if you are good at caring work and find it satisfying, this means that you are a very special kind of person. Our world, which is often so violent and cruel, so greedy and stupid, very much needs people like you. You are a real, whole person. It often seems that there are not so many of them around. You are someone who has dared to let the humanity within them reach out and touch the humanity of another. This is the most precious form of healing that we can offer today.

Much of this chapter is written mainly for family carers, although if you are a professional careworker, it would be a good idea to come to understand something new about the family members whom you meet in the course of your work, and you may discover something new about yourself. At the end of the chapter there is a section which deals with points that apply specially to professionals.

OUR NEEDS AS CARERS

If we are to care well, and to continue to care well through thick and thin, it is vital that our needs are met. What are these needs?

One is the need for a change, a break, for refreshment; having time when you are doing something completely different. So ask yourself: 'Do I do some things which I really enjoy, which bring benefit or happiness simply for me?' If the answer is yes, keep doing these things. Develop them so that they are an important part of your life. If the answer is no, then something is seriously missing. Give yourself some credit, and recognize that you too have needs.

You are not a saint or a martyr; you're simply a human being. Family carers may find it difficult to get the time away that they need. Help is available, through the Social Services, the Health Service, and perhaps through other agencies. Find out what arrangements can be made for you; this is a part of your rights as a citizen.

Another thing that you will need is the support of others. Caring can be lonely work, even when you are supposed to be part of a team. You are in contact with suffering, and it will get to you at times. You may feel a sense of dismay, or sadness, or even despair. Anxieties may be awakened in you: 'What if I become like this one day? What would it be like for me?' So if you are to carry on caring well, you need at least one person to whom you can really open up, someone who will listen to you and take care of you. Perhaps there are more people around who would be willing to do this than you realise.

ACCEPTING CHANGES

If we are close to someone, we probably have a strong investment in their staying as they are. People may even resist change that is positive, because it will upset the pattern they are used to. So as family members we may have great difficulty in accepting changes that come when one whom we know so well loses some of their mental powers. If we resist the changes, perhaps pretending to ourselves that they aren't happening, we will cause even more confusion and we will be seriously out of touch. So go along with the changes, while of course doing all you can to help the one you are caring for to remain in every sense a person. As you accept the changes you can be more relaxed. You will be changing too, perhaps gaining new strengths and insights.

DIFFICULT FEELINGS

Being with a relative who is severely confused can stir up many different feelings. Some of these may take you by surprise. Among them there may be:

-anger, when the one being cared for seems to be cut off, or difficult, or ungrateful

-disgust, when they do something that they would never have done before

-guilt, because you know that there's something you didn't do well, or didn't do at all

Maureen looked after her husband during his dementing illness. She had very little contact with others. When he was away at day care she cleaned the house, did the washing and went shopping. She felt there was no one with whom she could share her troubles. After a while she became very depressed . . .

-loneliness, a sense that no-one else really understands what you are feeling

-fear, not knowing what difficulties and pains may lie ahead

-envy, because other people you know are not having to go through this

-despair, because many of the good things you have known will not come back

Feelings such as these are perfectly natural and human. There's nothing wrong with you if you have them from time to time. Simply accept the feelings. But don't hold on to them - let them pass. It will not be good either for you or for others if you deny the feelings or try to block them off.

WHEN THERE'S NOT MUCH LOVE

There may be special difficulties if you do not really love the person you are looking after, or if old family conflicts are aroused, or if caring has been landed on you against your will. Again, be honest with yourself. You are not a saint, and many families have less love in them than we would wish. So recognize that in your mixed feelings there will be quite a lot that seems to be negative. Even so, you can still be an excellent caregiver. You may be able to 'work through' the negative part, and get closer than you have ever done before. Be realistic, too. You may need more professional help and more relief than others who took on caring out of love and free choice.

There is one further thing to mention. Family carers do sometimes get so upset that they are rough with the person they are looking after, or actually hit them. It's rather like when a parent 'batters' a child; frustration has built up to the point of explosion. If this has happened, it does not mean that you are wicked or evil, although perhaps you feel very guilty and ashamed. It does mean, though, that you are near the end of your tether, and need far more support than you are getting at present. It is best to say sorry to the one you have hurt - as tenderly as you can. You need to forgive yourself and, above all, you need to get help. It might be the time when full-time residential care would be best. Also, if you sense that you are coming near to the point where you might hit out, get help now, before you lose control. The more you know what you are feeling, the less likely you are to do something dangerous. There are many local carers' support groups available; you can find out the one nearest to you through your doctor, or through the organizations listed on page 96.

GETTING WHAT YOU WANT

If you are a family carer, you will need information and practical help. It's important that you do get all the support that's available, so that you remain in good health, both in body and mind. Sometimes carers struggle on alone because they "don't like to ask", or "don't want to be a nuisance". It's not often that help is given without it being asked for; and sometimes it only comes after a person has been very persistent. Knowing what may happen can make it easier to face. Being clear about what help is available, even before you actually need it, can be very reassuring. Don't assume that the doctor will have told you all that you need to know. Find out as much as you can. Sometimes family carers look after a loved one for several years, and then discover what they really needed to know when it is too late.

Many people feel intimidated by experienced professionals, such as doctors, receptionists, social workers and lawyers. If you are like this, you will need to learn a new skill - being assertive. This simply means knowing what you want and getting it, and doing so in a way that respects other people. Start by recognizing that you have a right to whatever help and information there may be available. Your needs and wishes are just as important as the next person's. Don't let yourself become one of those silent and self-sacrificing people who never gets what they want. Being like this won't really help either you or the person to whom you give care. Being assertive doesn't mean being pushy; it doesn't mean being selfish; it doesn't mean being inconsiderate of others; it doesn't mean asking for the impossible. By being assertive you can stand up for yourself and be strong in asking others to help you. You can look after yourself, and do it in a way that is just as fair to you as it is to others.

Here are some tips which might help you to be more assertive when dealing with professionals and others.

Josie had lived near her mother almost all her life. Josie had never married. Her sister was married and lived two hundred miles away. Somehow it was assumed by both sisters that Josie would look after their mother when her mental powers began to fail. Sometimes Josie felt rage, like a small, hurt child. Why should she do all this, when her mother had shown so little interest in her? Sometimes she felt terribly unwanted and unloved. Josie began to see a counsellor, and slowly came to recognize what a needy person she herself was. She made two new friends, with whom she was really honest. They both supported her. She learned to cope with her feelings, and she knew that her care for her mother improved. Then she insisted that her sister also took her share . . .

-Keep near the telephone a list of the numbers of all the people who can help, such as your doctor, social worker, district nurse, relatives, etc. When you need them, go ahead and phone. Remember, your time and efforts are just as valuable as theirs.

-Before contacting a professional by phone or in person, write out all your questions and any important information you want to convey. Have it handy so that you can refer to it.

-Keep a notebook, and bring it with you to appointments to jot down brief notes on what has been said. This will help you to ensure that you are getting the information you wanted. You may want to write things out more fully when you get home, while what went on at the meeting is still fresh in your mind.

-If you don't understand what someone has said to you, ask them to repeat it more plainly. If you still can't follow, ask if they would write it down for you. This often forces people into making things clear.

-If any of your questions can't be answered to your satisfaction, ask about who can answer them.

-You have the right to criticize the services provided for you and/or your loved one. When doing this, be fair and to the point and be constructive. Even if they might not be able to fix things in time to bring any benefit to you, you might be helping the next person.

▲ For Careworkers

In taking on caring work as a professional, there's much that seems to go against you. There are old, harsh attitudes, over-heavy duties, long hours, poor pay, and sometimes few prospects of promotion. Some carers cope with these difficulties by not bothering to give really personal care. They simply treat their work as a kind of low-grade child-minding, making sure that the people they are looking after are kept fairly clean, fairly quiet, and are given food and drink from time to time. Doing care work in this way gives a kind of protection; it seems to make the task possible. But in fact it often turns out to be boring, depressing and exhausting, and it brings no human reward. The other way of coping with the difficulties is to be aware, committed and involved. Somehow doing it this way is enlivening and full of interest, even though it will make us tired. The thing that keeps us feeling alive and sparky is having real contact with others, person-to-person, even in their suffering.

In taking up caring as a job, a big problem you may face is that few people really understand what you are doing. There is an ignorant view that suggests you are producing nothing, so your job has little value. People may not appreciate what caring involves, and often they are prejudiced against those who are confused, especially if they are elderly as well. Because of such attitudes you may have difficulty at times in feeling that your job is worthwhile, or even that you yourself have value. It doesn't help when the pay is generally far below what this kind of work deserves.

If there is an association of careworkers in your area, how about joining it? If there isn't one, could you and a few others form one? If you are thinking of making a commitment to your employer, insist on your right to know what are your prospects for advancement, and if possible get this stated in writing. Explore with your employer the possibilities for you to undertake further training. You may want to read up on what you are doing; if so, there are some excellent sources available, and a few of these are listed at the end of this book.

In some instances, you may discover that you understand quite a bit more about real, human caring than the people you work for. They may be content to simply provide shelter, food and some practical assistance to the people in their care; you, on the other hand, know that to care is to help people to a life worth living. Don't simply give up your ways because they're the boss. Caring for confused people may be one field in which employees need to teach their supervisors, every bit as much as the other way around. Try to find ways of approaching your supervisors or managers so that they will listen to you and accept what you have to say. Some of them may not have done much direct caring before, or they may come from the old school of thought on care. So be patient and persistent. If, despite your best efforts to improve your working conditions, you find that you are in a dead-end job where your employer has no real commitment to you and your

Fiona just began her job as a carer because she couldn't find other employment. It was simply a way of making some money. She soon found that she liked working with confused people. she began to read about their problems and took an evening course on the care of the elderly. As a result she decided to make her career in caring for those with failing mental powers. Eventually she became a manager of a residential home.

development, think carefully about whether you should be there. It may be best for you in the long run to begin looking for a place where your skills and expertise are better appreciated. We are going to need to put on continual pressure to raise the status of professional caregiving. It may be a long time before it is recognized as the supremely valuable work that it is, but change is occurring all the time.

THOUGHTS ON BEREAVEMENT

This chapter, like the last one, is mainly for family carers. But if you are a careworker of some kind, please keep reading. It may help you to understand what some of the family members whom you meet are going through. Also, you yourself may feel a sense of bereavement at the death or loss of someone who is in your care. You may have become especially attached to them, or their death may stir up a memory of some bereavement in the past.

As a family member, you will be having to face two bereavements, or possibly three, and the process of loss may go on for a long time.

First, there is the fact that you have a bond with someone whose mental powers are failing. That person is not now as you would have wanted or expected them to be. All relationships change over the years, and there have to be adjustments on both sides. Now it is you who are having to do most of the adjusting, and you don't know how it will end. Some of your hopes have come to nothing. You are suffering because of what you have lost. So this is a kind of bereavement, and you may be grieving already. You have sorrow for the person you are caring for; you have sorrow for a settled way of life that will never return; you have sorrow for yourself.

Then there's another bereavement, if your relative has to go into full-time residential care. Even when the decision is clearly the right one for both of you, something very important comes to an end at this point. However difficult it will have been for you as a carer at home, now there is a separation, and life may seem empty and alone. Visits to the nursing home, or wherever it is, will involve the pain of seeing the person you cared for having a new life without you, and each meeting will end with another parting. The time may come when you are not recognized, and you might wonder whether there's any point in visiting any more.

The third bereavement will come with the actual death of the person you cared for. Even though you may have already given them up in most ways, and even if your task as a carer was over some time before, a bond remains while they are alive. Against all appearances, there may still be a tiny spark of hope. But death really does mean the end, as far as this life is concerned. There's a last good-bye, a last letting go, to be faced.

Around these bereavements you may find yourself asking such questions as 'Why did this happen to us? Why is life so unfair? Is there any meaning in this? Why should such a life have to end in this way?' These are natural questions. You may not find clear answers. You may also start accusing yourself for all the things you didn't do. For some short periods you may feel drowned in sorrow and pain, as if your whole world is coming apart.

One simple guideline may help. 'Feel your feelings.' Be gentle to yourself, and allow yourself to grieve. Admit to yourself - and perhaps to a trusted friend - 'this is what I am really feeling.' It doesn't help to start saying 'I ought not to be feeling like this.' Our feelings tell us something of the truth, very frankly and directly. They can guide us into a true understanding .

Because the feelings around bereavement are so strange and powerful, people often go to great lengths to avoid them. Some try to keep a 'stiff upper lip', pretending that everything is normal. Others try to crowd out their feelings by becoming extremely busy, or taking up good causes. Others try to escape their feelings by actually going away. None of this really works, if it is done to escape from grieving. In fact, such ways of avoiding feelings can make a person depressed in the longer term. The truth is that the painful feelings around bereavement are there to be passed through, and there is no way round them. Those who do 'feel their feelings' find that the pain does get less, that comfort and strength do come, and that in course of time they can rebuild their lives. But it takes time.

Almost everybody needs human support when they are grieving. It may be ready to hand, through family, or friends, or neighbours, or those who share your faith. If you have been a very independent person, you may actually need to take steps to find the support you need. In many places there are support groups available. The Alzheimer's Disease Society may be able to help, or the organization for bereaved people called CRUSE (see pages 96 and 98). Many people who thought they were alright managing on their own, or who thought they just weren't the kind of person to join groups where people uncovered their feelings, have been surprised at how much help they found.

Losing a person whose mental powers had been failing is, in many

Things had never been easy between Phoebe and her father, Reluctantly, however, Phoebe agreed to look after him for a while when he was confused and ill. In the past, he had often moaned about his aches and pains. Now, in Phoebe's care, he was at it again. Phoebe thought this was part of the old pattern, but she did take her father to the doctor, who found nothing. The complaints continued, and Phoebe ignored them. The old man died soon afterwards, and was then found to have had cancer of the stomach. Phoebe could hardly live with herself. She felt a complete fraud, overwhelmed by bad feelings about herself. She began to see a counsellor, and gradually came to feel again that she was a worthwhile person, giving herself credit for the many good things she had done, and accepting what she had felt to be her failures.

Mr Larkin used to come regularly to the day care centre with his wife. It not only helped his wife to feel more secure there, but also he enjoyed giving a helping hand. He got on well with the staff, and they often said how much they appreciated his help. When Mrs Larkin died the staff sent him a sympathy card, but then he never heard from them again. He would have liked to continue his volunteer work at the centre, but they never invited him.

ways, far more difficult than losing someone who remained 'the person they were' right through until the point of death. The feelings are likely to be much more complicated, and the sorting out more difficult. You might need to find a counsellor. If you do this, it doesn't mean that you are abnormal; it simply means that you're sensible enough to recognize that you have a need.

Whatever your bereavement is like, give yourself time and space. You will need time, because grieving is a slow process. You will need space, so that the changes going on inside you can take place. It's difficult to accept, in the deepest layers of our hearts and minds, that a person we were close to has gone forever. If others are crowding in on you with their demands, it may be necessary to ask them to give you more consideration. Grief is like a river, taking its own course and going at its own pace. And there's a simple lesson: 'Don't try to push the river'.

▲ For Careworkers

If you have read through this chapter so far, you may be thinking of ways in which you might help family members when they are grieving. You might be able to put them in touch with a support group in your area. You may be able to lend an ear yourself. This may be specially comforting for them if you had been caring for the one they have lost; there is much that you might share.

Sometimes the relationships which form between careworkers and family members can end quite abruptly when the person who was being looked after dies. Try not to let this happen.

Careworkers are often among the best helpers for those who are bereaved. Perhaps it is time for some basic guidance in grief counselling to become part of their training.

A NEW KIND
OF CARER

In this book we have been describing things that many of the best carers feel deeply, but which have not yet been written down clearly and in detail. The heart of the matter is this. Good care is making the attempt to understand and establish continual contact; it involves filling out what is lacking, so that each confused individual remains a person. On the face of it, this sounds simple. We have seen a good deal of what it means in practice, as we have looked at different aspects of care, chapter by chapter. So as a carer, you are using and developing a wonderful range of skills. You are a kind of counsellor, a language interpreter, an occupational therapist, a personal assistant, an advocate, a nurse; all this and much more besides. Give yourself full credit for what you are doing.

But there is one further point to emphasize here. Good care is far more than doing things to or for another person. It also means developing awareness about ourselves.

-If we are to understand how a person feels when powerless, we need to know what being powerless does to us.

-If we are to understand their fear, and especially their fear of abandonment, we need to come to terms with our own deepest fears.

-If we are to understand their need to be taken care of, it is necessary to realize how much we need to be taken care of, too.

-If we are to understand what it is like for them to feel hopeless, it is necessary to face up to our own despair.

That's why caring goes so deep. Whenever we touch an area of need in another person, we find some echo of that need within ourselves. Where we cannot hear what is going on within ourselves, we may be closed off to some need within the other. So, as we learn to attend carefully both to the one we are caring for and to ourselves, we can become persons in a fuller sense. Although caring makes such heavy demands, and has its share of sorrow, we can still engage in it in a very positive way. Many family carers, when their work is done and the grief has begun to pass, find that they have become more dependable, compassionate and strong. They have grown and been enriched. In a different way, this is also true of those who commit themselves to caring work for pay, or as volunteers.

CHAPTER 16

WHERE TO
FIND HELP

There are some very good organizations which can give information and advice, and sometimes a great deal more. If you are a family carer, it is a good idea to get in touch with them as soon as you can. Probably there will be a local branch, which you can contact by telephone. They can tell you about all of the services available in your area, including financial and legal advice, and carer support groups. In addition, they offer lists of practical tips, as well as research updates and other publications. Here are the addresses of the national offices; these can put you in touch with your local branch, in case you have any difficulty in making contact.

Age Concern England
Astral House
1268 London Road
London SW 16 4 EJ
Telephone: 081-679 8000

Age Concern Wales
Fourth Floor
1 Cathedral Road
Cardiff CF1 9SD
Telephone: 0222-371566

Age Concern Scotland
54A Fountain Bridge
Edinburgh EH3 9PT
Telephone: 031-228 5656

Alzheimer's Disease Society
158-160 Balham High Road
London SW12 9BN
Telephone: 081-675 6557/8/9/0

Carers National Association
29 Chilworth Mews
London W2 3RG
Telephone: 071-724 7776

If you find you need help with caring for a relative in your home, contact your **local Social Services.** They may be able to provide you with a home help as well as meals-on-wheels, or assist you with arranging day care or respite care. Also, Social Services can help if it's a matter of arranging for a person to be taken into a residential home. You can find out the address and phone number of your local area office in the phone book.

If there are any medical problems, don't hesitate to contact **your doctor.** Also, **community psychiatric nurses** generally know a good deal about confusion. They may be able to offer you advice and reassurance. Ask your doctor to refer you. In some areas you can phone them directly.

The following organization, which operates in many parts of the country, may be able to provide you with a home carer. The address of the national office is:

Association of Crossroads
Care Attendant Schemes
10 Regent Place
Rugby Warwickshire
CV21 2PN
Telephone: 0788-573653

Benefits such as supplementary pensions, attendance allowance, and invalid care allowance are available through the **Department of Social Security**. Check the phone book for your nearest office. Making claims can sometimes be complicated, although often claims are completed without much difficulty. For help with claims contact your local Citizens Advice Bureau before you go to the DSS office. They are experts on these matters. Be sure you are getting everything you are entitled to by asking questions and being persistent. You can find the number of your local Citizens Advice Bureau in the phone book. The address of the central office is:

National Association of
Citizens Advice Bureaux
Middleton House
115-123 Pentonville Road
London N1 9LZ
Telephone: 071-833 2181

MIND mainly serves those with mental illness and their carers. However, they do have some useful information on caring, and some local branches provide advice and services on respite care. The address of the national office is:

MIND
(National Association for
Mental Health)
22 Harley Street
London W1N 2ED
Telephone: 071-637 0741

If the person you care for is incontinent, most health authorities have an incontinence adviser whom you can contact. The Disabled Living Foundation has a list of these, and can also provide you with information about wheelchairs, commodes, clothing, lifting equipment, special eating and drinking utensils, and a variety of other aids. The address of the central office is:

Disabled Living Foundation
380-384 Harrow Road
London W9 2HU
Telephone: 071-289 6111

If you need some additional occasional help, you might try the **Council for Voluntary Service**, listed in the telephone directory, or enquire if your **local church** has a scheme set up; many do. Your local Age Concern may also know of other volunteer groups in your area.

If you need someone to talk to who understands what you are going through, there are many counselling services and support groups available. Your doctor, Age Concern, Alzheimer's Disease Society, or Citizens' Advice Bureau can advise you on what there is in your area. Also, the **Samaritans** is a 24-hour telephone support service for anyone needing an understanding listener. Their number is listed in the telephone directory. And, CRUSE specializes in bereavement counselling services. They have many local branches but the central address is:

CRUSE
126 Sheen Road
Richmond
Surrey TW9 1UR
Telephone: 081-940 4818

The important thing is to start finding out, and then be assertive. Each local area is different, but each area does have ways of giving support to family carers. Once you have stared to explore, you'll discover that one contact leads on to another.

SUGGESTIONS FOR FURTHER READING

GOOD SHORT PUBLICATIONS, APPROPRIATE FOR FAMILY AND OTHER CARERS:

Who Cares? Information and Support for the Carers of Confused People, 1986. Published by Health Education Authority and available by writing to Who Cares?, PO Box 807, London SE99 6YE.

Caring for the Person with Dementia: A Guide for Familes and Other Carers, by Chris Lay and Bob Woods, 1989. Available from the Alzheimer's Disease Society, 156-160 Balham Road, London SW12 9BN.

Caring for Confusion by Paulette Micklewood, 1991. Published by Scutari Press.

Alzheimer's: Caring for Your Loved One, Caring for Yourself, by Sharon Fish, 1991. Published by Lion Publications.

COMPREHENSIVE GUIDES APPROPRIATE FOR ALL TYPES OF CARERS:

Working with Dementia, edited by Graham Stokes and Fiona Goudie, 1990. Published by Winslow Press, Telford Road, Bicester, Oxon OX6 OTS.

Living With Alzheimer's Disease and Similar Conditions, by Gordon Wilcock, 1990. Published by Penguin.

Dementia and Mental Illness in the Old, by Elaine Murphy, 1986. Published by Papermac.

36 Hour Day: Caring at Home for Confused Elderly People, by Nancy L. Mace and others, 1985. Published by and available from Age Concern, Astral House, 1268 London Road, London SW16 4EJ.

Living with Dementia, by John Riordan and Bob Whitmore, 1990. Published by Manchester University Press.

Care for the Carer, by Christine Orton, 1989. Published by Thorsons Publishing Group.

Confusion in Old Age, by John Wattis, 1988. Published by The British Medical Association and available through the Alzheimer's Disease Society.

BOOKS FOR THE PROFESSIONAL CARER:

Working With Dementia: Guidelines for Professionals, edited by Mary Marshall, 1990. Published by Venture Press.

Living with Dementia: Community Care of the Elderly Mentally Infirm by Chris J. Gilleard, 1984. Published by Croom Helm.

Family Work with Elderly People, by Alison Froggatt, 1990. Published by MacMillan.

Validation: the Feil Method by Naomi Feil, 1992. English edition published by Winslow Press.